MEL BAY PRESENTS

THE ART OF HAWAIIAN STEEL GUITAR

By Stacy Phillips

Forewords by Bob Brozman
and DeWitt Scott

Over 50 great solos with detailed analyses and historical background.

This book is dedicated to my sister, Rochelle Marshall, for her unconditional support.

Contents

Acknowledgments

To Sean Coane, Chris Davis, and Rachel Dembar — the best kind of students — the kind that teach the teacher.

To George Youngblood — for access to his collection of old sheet music and instruction books.

To Bob Brozman — for inspiration.

To DeWitt Scott Sr. — for information and support.

To Dirk Vogel — *the* source for traditional Hawaiian-style steel guitar — for information and access to his record collection.

Foreword

Having played some of the arrangements in this book I feel like Stacy is right on target for the players that would like to learn about the authentic Hawaiian style of music. There are two types of Hawaiian music, the "authentic style" and "tourist" Hawaiian music. Stacy is presenting to you the "authentic style" and is much needed to help keep the Hawaiian music alive. He presents some unusual bar slants, and this is good, as well as acquainting you with the beautiful harmonics that are so necessary in Hawaiian music. The book is well presented and he leaves no doubt on how to play each page as he explains in detail how to get the most out of each arrangement as well as giving a short history about the Hawaiian steel guitar music as the book progresses. You will have to exert yourself but the end result will be well worth it!

DeWitt (Scotty) Scott
International Steel Guitar Convention
Saint Louis, Missouri

Hawaiian guitar is the most mysterious of all string instruments. No two players have the same touch or tone. Since the initial explosion (1915) in the popularity of this intensely personal instrument, the Hawaiian guitar has left its mark on many styles of music, including jazz, blues, Western swing and country.

Most players have learned by ear from the recordings of the masters. In fact, it is a good idea for any student to supplement transcriptions with the recorded versions of materials. All the original virtuosos are gone now, with the exception of Tau Moe, now in his 80s and living on Oahu. Fortunately a healthy body of recordings and reissues still remains.

General curiosity about Hawaiian guitar has increased over the past few years, probably as a result of the recent availability of the reissues of old 78s as well as a general upswing in the popularity of "World Music." Through my work with the instrument, I have encountered any number of younger players interested in the fascinating, older style of playing.

Stacy Phillips is highly qualified to write this book. His past volumes have aided countless Dobro players in unraveling the secrets of that instrument. He has now applied his great ears and musical sensibilities to penning the first real Hawaiian guitar instruction book published since the Golden Age. Despite our long-running and good-natured dispute about the nature of tone and vibrato, I will admit to Stacy I have looked over the transcriptions and the notes are all there!

Quite seriously, Mr. Phillips has used skill and impeccable judgment, both in selections of musical works and in accuracy of transcription. He is to be thanked wholeheartedly for carrying on the history of this hauntingly unique instrument: the Hawaiian guitar.

Aloha,
Bob Brozman
1991

Maka Mua
"Beginning"

In my early days as a Dobroist I was only peripherally aware of a particularly Hawaiian style of playing steel. Then, one day I visited Robert Gear in a recording studio where he was preparing the first Hawaiian-guitar reissue album, *Hula Blues* (Rounder 1012). "Listen to this," he said, and played Jim and Bob's version of **"Home on the Range."** By the time the last chorus was over, I realized that I had stopped breathing and had begun to foam at the mouth and flap my ears — a truly transcendental musical orgasm! (See *The Dobro Book* in the bibliography for a transcription of this tour de force.)

Needless the say, I have been hooked on this stuff ever since. Now I wait in vain for old Charlie Chan films and other Hollywood potboilers like *Waikiki Wedding, Bird of Paradise,* and *Hawaii Calls* for fleeting sounds of Sol Hoopii, Andy Iona, or Dick McIntire. By the end of the book you should understand why.

Stacy Phillips (photo by Georgia Sheron)

Steel guitar in its many forms is probably enjoying its greatest popularity at this time, but it is only with a recent spate of reissues of some early recordings that steel played in the Hawaiian manner is once again receiving attention. It is ironic that it has taken so long for the original style to be rediscovered. This book will, hopefully, increase your awareness of the wealth of beautiful Hawaiian music, music that inspired the invention of the steel guitar.

The majority of the tablatures here are pre-1940, but styles since then are represented. The tunes are arranged to benefit steelers of all stripes, strings, and styles, whether acoustic or electric.

First, here are some definitions to ensure that we all are on the same wavelength: **Hawaiian guitar, lap steel,** and **steel guitar** all refer to instruments played flat, facing upwards, and fretted with a contrivance of metal usually called a **bar.** Lap steel ordinarily denotes an electric, solid-body version. The pedal steel is an outgrowth of the lap steel — with very little visual resemblance to a guitar. It uses foot pedals and knee levers to alter the pitch of the strings.

Dobro and National are the most popular brands of acoustic Hawaiian guitars used today. These are resophonic guitars, with light-weight aluminum dishes inside their body chambers. The wooden Dobro has one large "cone." The metal-bodied National model most popular with Hawaiians in the 1920s and '30s has three smaller dishes and is referred to as a "tricone."

The transcriptions in this book accurately represent the styles of many of the greatest names in Hawaiian guitar. **Most of the music is in today's standard acoustic-steel tuning of G major, starting from the first, highest-pitched, thinnest string: D-B-G-D-B-G.** Some players use an equivalent A major: E-C♯-A-E-C♯-A. If you prefer this, you can still use the G-tuning tablature. Play as written, but then raise the given chord symbols by 2 frets (e.g., C to D, or E♭ to F).

Because a variety of retunings is endemic to this instrument, several arrangements in each of the most popular forms are presented in their own chapters.

Buy some of the records listed in the discography. Written music is a road map. You have to hear the sounds in your head before you will be able to duplicate them truly on your guitars.

The tunes in this book were selected (within the constraints of copyright laws) on the basis of their status as standards in the genre, as examples of particular techniques and styles, and simply whether I was attracted to the melody.

You are now ready for some preliminaries. Simply chant the passwords to one of the ancient hula schools.

"E hea i ke kanaka e komo maloko e hanai ai a hewa ka waha."

"Call the person to enter, feed him until he can take no more."

Read on. Great music awaits.

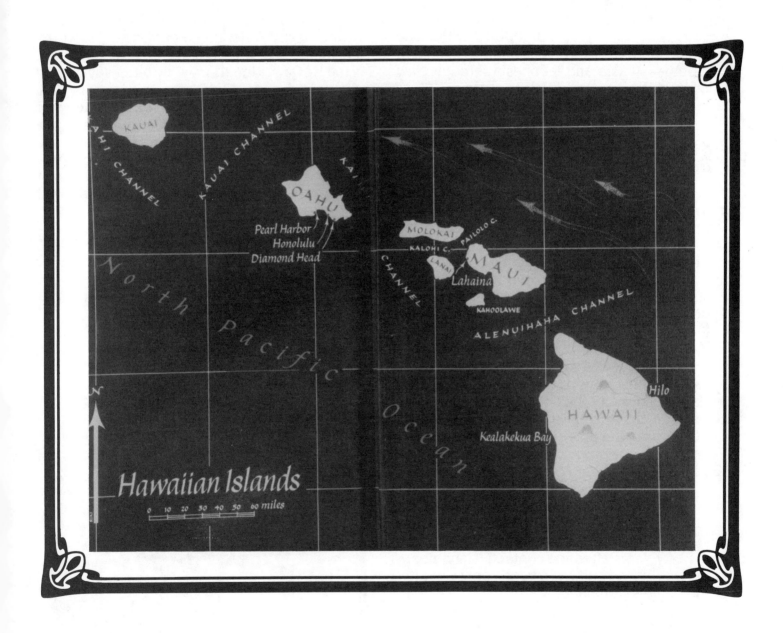

A Background to Hawaiian History to the End of World War II

Hawaii is an American state like no other. The archipelago stretches for 1600 miles and includes islands with such resonant names as Midway, Maui, Hermes Atoll, and Disappearing Island.

Hawaii was the last major area of Polynesia to be settled, between the years 400 and 600, by way of the Marquesas Islands. A wave of Tahitian migration occurred around 1000 to 1300. The ultimate origins of the Polynesians are thought to be Southeast Asia and Indonesia through New Guinea and then to the Fiji Islands between 4000 and 2000 B.C.E. The name *"Hawai'i"* may mean "little (i'i) Java" (the "j" having shifted to an "h," and the Hawaiian "w" pronounced as "v").

Before Western contact the Islands were not politically united, and brutal warfare was common. But the population did live in harmony with the ecology of its environment. With the arrival of James Cook's British exploring expedition in 1778, all this changed. During his second stop-over, in a classic case of cross-cultural misconceptions and confusion, Cook was bludgeoned to death and disemboweled as a failed god.

One of the warriors present at this death was Kamehameha, who took advantage of the technological know-how of some of Cook's shipmates to usurp and then consolidate power. He conquered the major islands by 1795 and in 1810 became the first king of a unified Hawaii. Westerners were made chief advisors to the now Kamehameha I.

Millennia of isolation made Hawaiians easy prey for imported contagions like measles, smallpox, venereal diseases, as well as alcoholism. Forty years after first contact, Island population was halved and, in 75 years, only a quarter of the natives remained!

The enormous change in world view that accompanied the appearance of the West led to a royal family-instigated dissolution of some of the foundations of Hawaiian religion, shortly after the death of Kamehameha I in 1819. Less than a year later, Protestant missionaries from New England arrived and were able to take advantage of the spiritual and political upheaval. Hawaii soon became an important whaling port, while its sandalwood forests were decimated for export to China. Christians taught the natives the concept of sin and to be ashamed of their own culture. A textbook situation of benevolent cultural genocide was well underway.

Once granted a foothold, Westerners (by 1850, mostly Americans) burrowed deeply into the politics and burgeoning capitalistic economy of the Hawaiian kingdom. One bitter saying from this period goes, "The missionaries told us to look up to heaven and, while we did, they stole our land." As a result of the Great *Mahele* (land division) swindle of 1850, ethnic Hawaiians suddenly found themselves with rights to only a minuscule portion of the land. Bloated plantations carved out generous portions of fertile soil.

Left to right: Robert Louis Stevenson and King David Kalakaua (courtesy Phil Zimmerman)

Sugar became the economic bastion of the new American plutocracy (mostly descendants of the original missionaries). The native kingship ruled only so long as it did not interfere with King Sugar's profits.

Aboriginal Hawaiians were deemed inappropriate workers for the plantations, so first Chinese, then Portuguese, Japanese, and finally Filipino labor was imported in a search for sufficiently tractable indentured servants.

When David Kalakaua was crowned king in 1874, the seeds were planted for an eventual showdown with American interests, who were already conniving for some official connection with the States. Kalakaua favored appointing indigenous Hawaiians to administrative offices. He began the royal-family patronage of Hawaiian culture, including music, and championed a resurgence of some of the "old ways." He alternately intrigued with and antagonized various factions of local businesspeople. Anti-colonialism became a political factor.

In 1887, while their private militia surrounded government buildings, the planters usurped most of the king's remaining powers. The threat of revolution and counter-revolution was in the air.

King Kalakaua died in California in 1891 shortly after delivering a farewell to the Hawaiian people into a newly invented Edison phonograph. His sister became Queen Lili'uokalani (the author of *"Aloha Oe"*). Before her plans to regain some royal prerogatives were realized, the planters sprung a coup with the help of some Marines who "happened" to be anchored off shore. Hopes of becoming an American protectorate were temporarily dashed when Congress and President Grover Cleveland refused to recognize the insurrection. A republic of sorts was proclaimed in 1894. A royalist rebellion was easily crushed, and the former queen was jailed.

By 1898 imperialism and expansionism were in vogue in America, and William McKinley's administration was able to pass a bill making the Hawaiian archipelago a territory of the United States. Ethnic Hawaiians were completely eliminated from any real power in the political system. By old-fashioned intimidation and political chicanery, the plutocracy, now a sugar and pineapple monopoly called The Big Five, held onto unrivalled power until after World War II. Then labor unions (whose memberships were largely descendants of imported plantation workers) won some key strikes, which signalled the end of political domination by the old-line powers.

Democratization of Hawaii had begun, but only *just.* Ethnic Hawaiians are still mostly passive players in the political and economic life of the Islands. Happily, this is not so in the case of music.

An Introduction to Hawaiian Music

Just what is meant when a steel guitarist is said to be playing "Hawaiian style"? Foremost, this music is a successful amalgam of Polynesian, European, and North American melodies and rhythms. Assuming the reader is familiar with some basic properties of Western music, let us examine what is known about the distinguishing features of "pure" Hawaiian music.

Typically in such fusions, it is the native vocal style that is the least-assimilated quality. The influence of the old manner of singing on Hawaiian guitar is made more evident in the chapter, "Characteristics of Hawaiian-Style Steel Guitar." Hopefully the connection will convince you to do some careful listening to the Islands' great vocalists.

Much of this chapter is based on the research and writings of Elizabeth Tatar, ethnomusicologist with the Bishop Museum in Honolulu.

Left to right: **Sanford Dole (a leader of the planter "aristocracy"), Henry Berger, and ex-queen Lydia Lili'uokalani** (courtesy Phil Zimmerman)

We do not know with certainty what Hawaiians sounded like before Captain Cook's landing in 1778; but, as the result of recent research, some characteristics can be described with confidence. Luckily, some recordings were made of Hawaiian chanters born before 1850 and who lived in relative isolation from Western influence.

Island language had no term for music as such, but many for various styles of chanting, vocal inflections, rhythms, and instruments. "Chanting" refers to the ancient form of *mele* ("chanted poetry," although now the word often means "song"). There are *mele oli* (unaccompanied chant) and *mele hula* (chant accompanied with dancing and/or instruments). They deal with all aspects of Hawaiian social and religious life. For the purposes of this book, the musical aspects of chanting (as opposed to their texts) bear more directly on the development of the sound of the steel guitar.

In Western terms, the melodies of the chants are very simple. In fact, it is possible that Hawaiians learned the concept of the melodic line from Westerners. Here are some relevant traits of the old vocal style:

1. All chants are in major keys. (I am unaware of any unambiguous exceptions.)

2. The harmonies are simple, perhaps just fifth intervals (e.g., the interval between a G and a D), but possibly thirds (G to B) and fourths (G to C).

3. Vocal vibratos of different qualities are essential.

4. There are glottal cut-offs of vowels (related to the early style of staccato phrasing on steel?).

5. Vocal glides are common (obviously related to steel slides).

6. Chanters made vocal "breaks" *(ha'i)*, jumping up in pitch like yodelers. Falsetto *(leo ki'eki'e)* has been an integral part of Hawaiian vocals for a long time, but it probably became a staple as a result of Western influence. A possible native source of this head-tone singing is the pre-contact chants which have "conversa-

tions" between male and female characters as part of the lyrics. Male chanters may have used falsetto for the latter. (These effects are also imitated by steel guitars.)

7. Trills and wailing (*uweuwe*) mannerisms are used (the source of the steel's tremolo?).

The only pre-contact string instrument is the *ukeke,* a three-string mouth bow (the mouth cavity is used as a resonating chamber). Drums and flutes are more common. Among the typical instruments are:

1. *Ipu* — gourd drum
2. *Pahu* — drum of a sharkskin membrane over a hollowed log
3. *Uliuli* — a whirring rattle
4. *Pu* — conch shell
5. *Puniu* — coconut-shell drum
6. *Ohe hano ihu* — nose flute

Musicians also made percussive sounds by striking various parts of their bodies.

The arrival of missionaries in 1820 began Western musical influence in earnest. They taught *himeni* (hymns) in choral arrangements. These introduced four- and eight-measure phrases and European harmony. With the establishment of Hawaii as a whaling port, the secular music of sailors also became an avenue of acculturation. The melodies of old sea shanties can be heard in some old Hawaiian tunes. Mexican, Portuguese, Italian, German, and even Burmese music was heard by the Hawaiians in this period.

The importation of cattle herds and their attendant Mexican and Portuguese *paniolos* (slang for "cowboys," derived from *Español*) to Hawaii Island may have introduced falsetto technique. Violin and flute were popular lead instruments, and ships' bands introduced brass instruments and the march and waltz forms.

A truly new fusion of music was realized in the years of 1870 to 1900. The royal family became not only patrons of the new form but also some of its foremost authors of songs. Novel categories of music appeared: *himeni*-like secular tunes and *mele hula kui* (chant-derived, Westernized music, *"kui"* denoting a joining of the old and new) were generated in the cultural maelstrom of that period. Western-style cadences which evolved into the typical Hawaiian turn-around or vamp became part of the sound.

The Spanish guitar was introduced at the beginning of this era, and the basis was laid for the development of a native slack-key style (*kiho alu*).

As a result of a fascination with ships' bands, King Lot Kamehameha hired a Prussian musician named Henry Berger to reorganize and upgrade the Royal Hawaiian Band. Besides arranging the typical light classical airs and marches of the time, Berger made himself aware of the emerging character of Hawaiian music. He hired ethnic Islanders as band members. Berger was the first to collect tradition-based melodies and set them down in standard musical notation. He also tutored the royal family in the rudiments of Western music. He is considered by many as the most influential individual in the original synthesis of Polynesian and Western forms.

Around 1900, another phase in the development of modern Hawaiian music began. Contact between the mainland and Islands increased many fold. Ragtime entered as an influence. Strings replaced winds as instruments of choice. The steel guitar and ukulele had recently been invented and were quickly absorbed into the euphonious melange. Songs with mostly English lyrics and pop and ragtime accompaniment first appeared, and with them the burgeoning *hapa haole* (half-white) style burst forth. (*"Haole"* seems to be connected with "spiritlessness." At first sight, Hawaiians thought that people with such fair skin might be ghosts.) In early arrangements in this style, saxophones played the role that steel guitars soon appropriated.

In 1915, Hawaiian string-music combos participated in San Francisco's Panama-Pacific International Exhibit, an extravaganza that celebrated the opening of the Panama Canal. At that time, such fairs and expositions were major venues for disseminating the latest trends and exotic national identities. The new Territory of Hawaii invested heavily in its pavilion; and, as a result of mainland exposure to the sounds, Island music, both *mele kui* and *hapa haole,* infected a generation of Americans.

First-generation steelers Pale K. Lua, Frank Ferera, and the putative inventor of Hawaiian guitar, Joseph Kekuku, all performed in San Francisco and, for non-Hawaiians, steel guitar became synonymous with Polynesian music.

9

A craze for *hapa haole* tunes reached epidemic proportions. Tin Pan Alley hacks spewed out such forgettable opuses as **"Yacka Hula Hicka Dula," "Wicki Wacki Woo," "Wooly Woo,"** and **"Hula Lou."** Instead of *hapa haole,* much of this output was 99% vapidity.

The steel guitar quickly became accepted in what was then "modern-traditional" country music, as well. Jimmie Rodgers' occasional Hawaiian accompanists, as well as Jimmy Tarlton and Cliff Carlisle, made the sound of the steel fashionable in the rural Southeast, while Bob Dunn and Leon McAuliffe did the same for the Southwest. A direct line runs from these pioneers to the modern mechanical marvel known as the pedal steel guitar.

Both ethnic and non-ethnic Hawaiians adapted to 1920s jazz and blues. These musicians did not swallow the American form whole, but evolved a unique Polynesian version. For many years *hapa haole* records were the most popular items in recording-company catalogs. Native players found work not only on the mainland, but everywhere there was a European presence.

By 1930 the fever had subsided, but Hawaiian music remained a staple in the continental United States. Hotels and Polynesian and Chinese restaurants all featured revues of varying degrees of questionable authenticity. The *hapa haole* style developed a big-band sound. In Hawaii the tourist age began, and the music attended the visitors. **"Hawaii Calls"** inaugurated a decades-long radio show beaming music to the mainland.

Meanwhile there were currents of musical sharing occurring throughout Polynesia. Tahitian and Samoan influence were felt, and a number of these islands' tunes merged into the Hawaiian repertoire. (In fact, much of what is now performed under the rubric of hula is of recent import from elsewhere in the Pacific. The raffia hula skirts now so associated with Hawaii actually derive from Tahiti and the Gilbert Islands.)

As the 1960s approached, Hawaiian music underwent a dramatic plunge in popularity and almost totally disappeared from the public ear. Mainland rock and roll was in firm control, and it was not until "ethnic identity" became a buzz word in the early 1970s that tradition-based music experienced a local renaissance. Now the State of Hawaii has its own hit parade that features further amalgams with world music. Can you dig reggae-Hawaiian?

Outside the Islands, however, the music is still virtually invisible. (Do you remember any Hawaiian music in the soundtrack of the old television show *Hawaii Five-O?*) Fortunately, there still are some enthusiasts and Hawaiian music clubs to keep a faint chang-a-lang rhythm and steel slide murmuring in the background of the noise of our post-modern industrial society.

Harry Owens and His Orchestra with Alvin Isaacs on steel (courtesy Dirk Vogel)

A History of the Hawaiian Guitar

[This chapter is an abridgment of an entry in *Hawaiian Music and Musicians: An Illustrated History*, edited by George S. Kanahele, © 1979, University of Hawaii Press. Reprinted by permission of the publisher. Bracketed comments are by this author.]

Origins

Hawaii, appropriately, has been accepted as the birthplace of the Hawaiian steel guitar. But precisely when, how, or by whom it was invented have been unsettled questions. There are three conflicting claims attributing the invention of the steel guitar to three different persons: James Hoa, Gabriel Davion, and Joseph Kekuku.

[The evidence for Hoa is based on uncorroborated testimony, and there is circumstantial evidence against his candidacy.]

The Davion claim is a little more intriguing. The first and so far the only documented source of the story is a statement by the composer Charles E. King, who said during one of his radio-station KGU broadcasts in the late 1930s, "In 1884 I was living at Waihe'e, Maui, and there appeared in the village a group of musicians from Honolulu, one of whom was Gabriel Davion — a young man who was born in India, kidnapped by a sea captain, and finally brought to Honolulu.... This Davion attracted a great deal of attention because he had a new way of playing the guitar.... All the playing was done on one string, and the strings were not elevated...."

Although King was already in his sixties when he recounted his boyhood experience (he was only 10 years old in 1884) with Davion, he was still alert and his memory good. Since we cannot fault him on any other ground, his claim must be taken seriously. The fact that Davion came from India is significant, for he might well have learned the sliding technique using a rod or hard substance from Indian players of the *gottuvadyam*. [This is a sitar-like instrument from southern India. It is played on the lap with a slide of ebony, glass, or even bison's horn. It is not a very well-known instrument, even in India. Currently, perhaps the best-known player is Ravi Kirin, who occasionally tours the United States.] It would have been a relatively simple matter of using it with a guitar. Even if James Hoa did invent the steel guitar as early as 1876, or Davion in 1884, still unexplained is the long gap between its first appearance and popularization by other Hawaiian guitarists — a period of 10 to 20 years.

With Joseph Kekuku, we have no such dilemma. The evidence is more plentiful and convincing that he not only discovered but also developed and popularized the new steel-guitar technique. There are numerous stories on record of the early attempts by the young Kekuku to develop the steel guitar. Kekuku is said to have told a guitar enthusiast in London in 1919 that he produced his first steel-guitar sound in 1885 at the age of 11. He was walking along the railway strumming his guitar, according to his story, when he picked up a bolt, slid it across the guitar strings, and effected the characteristic slur of the steel. He went home and practiced the sound with a penknife and, later, even the blade of a straight razor with the edge ground down.

We have statements from his fellow students at Kamehameha School for Boys, where he enrolled in 1889 at the age of 15, confirming his skills. Simon Nawaa, who was ahead of Kekuku, said: "To our astonishment, Joe, besides playing the guitar the ordinary way, would shift to running a hair comb or tumbler on the strings, producing a sweet sound, while Sam (his cousin), the accompanist, followed him on the violin."

Kekuku progressed from bolt, pocket comb, knife, and tumbler to the steel bar which he designed and made himself in the school shop. In developing his new-found technique, Kekuku raised the strings of his guitar to enable the steel bar to glide along without touching the frets. He also switched from gut to wire strings because they sustained the tones longer.

He showed off his playing for classmates and in concerts in Honolulu and thus began to popularize the steel guitar. After leaving Kamehameha School, Kekuku became a musician and in 1904 left for the U.S. mainland, as did many other Hawaiians, to entertain. He toured not only the mainland, but Europe as well.

However difficult it may be to reconcile these three conflicting claims, it is reasonable to argue that Hoa, Davion, and Kekuku may have discovered the technique independently. After all, Hawaiians had the guitar since the early 1800s and had been innovative guitarists. By the last quarter of the century, the slack-key style had probably already appeared, and the shift from that to steel-guitar technique would not have been difficult. Others may have stumbled upon the new steel technique, too, without having been noticed. It would not be the first time the title of inventor has had to be shared.

Development

Three important elements went into the development of the steel guitar: mechanical innovations, new tunings, and techniques or styles of playing. The basic instrument was the acoustic Spanish guitar, but the new sound required at least three simple mechanical innovations. The first was the bar, which was made of steel, ivory, or other hard substances. Because of its availability and sound-producing qualities, however, the steel bar was preferred.

The second innovation was an adapter placed over the top fret [nut] in order to raise the strings by about a quarter inch so as to eliminate the noise caused by the bar coming in contact with the frets. The adapter was usually made from a piece of wood.

The third and last mechanical addition was the pick. While Spanish-guitar players could use fingers or fingernails, the steel guitarist needed a harder material than bare fingers to get a "bite." So Kekuku and his contemporaries designed finger and thumb picks cut out of metal and shaped them to fit their fingers.

The next technical addition did not come until the early 1920s when the National and Dobro resonators appeared on the market. The resonator was a metal vibrating disc in place of the sound hole. In the construction of the Dobro, a wooden bridge was placed on a cast-aluminum spider [in the shape of a spider web], which was in direct contact with the resonator and fastened to it by a screw. Playing the strings produced a vibration through the spider to the resonator, causing the Dobro's louder, sustained tone. The National guitar was equipped with three [smaller] metal-disc resonators and produced a slightly different metallic sound.

Although manufactured on the U.S. mainland, the new guitars won immediate popularity with Hawaiian steel guitarists. Pale K. Lua, Sol Hoopii, Joe Kekuku, and many others became champions of the National. They liked the new instrument with its all-metal body which, when spotlighted on the performing stage, was spectacular to watch. But what they liked most were the greater volume and sustained tone, allowing greater glissando and vibrato — elements which made the steel guitar unique.

The most common tuning first used by Hawaiian guitarists was the so-called low bass A tuning of, from bass to treble, E-A-E-A-C♯-E. This and other tunings were generally taken from slack-key tunings since guitarists were most familiar with these. Later a variation of it, the high-bass tuning of A-C♯-E-A-C♯-E, was also used.

The early style of playing the steel was influenced by several factors. One was the use of slack-key tunings, which meant that the bass strings were tuned to a tonic-dominant combination. [Tonic to dominant is a I chord to V chord progression; e.g., G to D.] The style was thus very much like that of slack key: a plucked

Joseph Kekuku (courtesy Tony Todaro)

melody was accompanied by an alternating bass. A basic difference was evident from the start, however. Rather than developing short melodic motifs interwoven into a strong rhythmic bass, the steel played the entire melody from start to finish, somewhat in imitation of the voice.

The style was characterized by a staccato approach, interspersing open strings with melodic tones. This was dictated by the nature of the acoustic guitar, which did not allow sustainment of long notes.

Electrification

The first electric steel guitar to be marketed was the Rickenbacker — and it caused a sensation. Called the "frying pan" or "pancake" because of its shape, it had a circular cast-aluminum sound box and a single neck, with an electric pickup and volume control but no tone control. Its big sound, tone clarity, maximum sustainment of notes, and new technical and stylistic possibilities made many instant converts. In Hawaii, despite its high cost — $69.50 per instrument without the amplifier — sales were lively.

By the late 1930s, the Rickenbacker was overtaken by other models such as the National and Gibson, shaped like a "biscuit box," which we now associate with the steel guitar. The new design consisted of a wide fretboard, an electric pickup, and strings raised high above the board. The new models had either six or eight strings and were equipped with four legs. This change not only brought about clearer amplification: it freed the guitarist's legs and opened the way for more strings, multiple necks, and pedals.

[The evolution of the pedal steel guitar is a story of engineering triumphs and additional strings that continues today. Since this species of guitar is peripheral to Hawaiian music, its story must be told another time.]

Electrification brought about not only mechanical developments, but also changes in tuning, playing technique, and style. The new steel players developed an almost infinite variety of tunings. With the addition of multiple necks, a variety of different tunings could be used at once.

Playing techniques and styles were also changed, if not revolutionized. The old staccato style was supplanted by what might be called

Cover of a 1927 steel-guitar book published by Wm. J. Smith Music Company, New York City (courtesy George Youngblood)

nahenahe or "sweet" style using more slides, chord suspensions, and prolonged tremolos — a style reminiscent of the playing of Dick McIntire, made possible by the electrified steel. With the capability of volume control, Hawaiian guitarists developed a characteristic style of attacking a pitch on the string accompanied by various degrees of dynamic changes, especially when executed with a slide. The manipulation of loudness and softness on the attack is still a very individual trademark of contemporary players.

Hawaiian guitarists, however, could not accept all the consequences of electrification — particularly certain aspects of the pedal steel. With their multiple levers, pedals, necks, and sophisticated technology demanding a knowledge of mechanics and engineering, the advanced pedal steel models have not often appeared in Hawaiian ensembles. Basically, the reasons have been more practical than aesthetic or philosophical. For one thing, these models are too inconvenient to move around, especially for the many musicians in Hawaii who play casual dates. They are, moreover, expensive, costing as much as $2000. And for many they are simply too complicated to play. More than one guitarist feels that heavy technology has reduced the personality of the instrument and lessened the importance of techniques and nuances that took years to develop and master. Nevertheless, outstanding Hawaiian steel players such as Jules Ah See, Ernest Tavares, and Billy Hew Len have used pedal steel guitars.

[This apology for the lack of use of the pedal steel in Hawaiian music could have been written in 1938 by acoustic players about electric instruments. It seems to me that its absence from the scene is at least as much a reflection of the lack of opportunity for steel players to make a good living in Hawaii. When they make as much money as semi-professional country pedal steel players, and if steel again becomes a necessity, the local musicians will probably take to creating extensions of Hawaiian-style playing with the latest machines available.]

Popularization

In Hawaii, the steel guitar caught on in the late 1890s or early 1900s, for by then we hear of steel-guitar playing as part of the Hawaiian music scene. Pale K. Lua, a contemporary and friend of Joseph Kekuku (both were born and raised in the town of La'ie), must have been playing steel by the turn of the century. Frank Ferera was playing, too, prior to 1902 when he left for the U.S. mainland. We also know that in 1899 either Tom Hennessey or July Paka played the steel guitar when they made their first recording for Edison in San Francisco.

From Hawaii the steel guitar moved to the mainland and then to other parts of the world, where it became synonymous with Hawaiian music. The steel was introduced to the mainland early — in 1899 by July Paka, in 1902 by Frank Ferera, and in 1904 by Joseph Kekuku himself, followed by almost every notable Hawaiian-steel guitarist over the next two or three decades. Some, like Kekuku, Lua, and Ferera, never returned to Hawaii. They played in vaudeville, chautauquas, clubs and theaters, expositions, and so on, throughout the U.S. and Canada. Great numbers of people in small towns and big cities first heard the steel in this way. Many of these troubadours settled down long enough in major cities to open up music studios for the steel guitar.

By 1920 or so, the steel guitar was part of the Hawaiian-music craze that was sweeping the American continent. Publishers put out instruction books for steel guitar. Many offered correspondence courses with various attractive bonuses for completion, including steel guitars. Mail-order houses began to sell thousands of guitars — first acoustic, then amplified — plus folios of popular songs. The Oahu Company, for example, during the 1930s sold guitars, lessons, and sheet music to millions of people around the world.

The trickle of steel recordings started in the early 1900s turned into a torrent in the 1920s and 1930s. By the mid-'30s, radio stations in Halifax, Tokyo, Hilversum (Netherlands), and Batavia (Jakarta) were carrying regular programs of Hawaiian music dominated by the sound of steel.

An epidemic of Hawaiian guitars swept the country (photo courtesy of Phil Zimmerman)

Decline and Revival

From its apogee of popularity in the 1930s, the Hawaiian steel guitar experienced a steady decline in popular interest around the world. This decline paralleled that of Hawaiian music, and some believe there is a definite cause-and-effect relationship.

This view may very well apply in the international context where the steel has been equated with Hawaiian music. The view may not be applicable to Hawaii, however, where the steel has been regarded as only one of several lead instruments in the Hawaiian ensemble.

It is not easy to pinpoint the beginning of this decline, but it clearly coincided with the invasion of rock and roll into the Islands in the 1950s and 1960s. By the beginning of the 1970s, the steel guitar had reached its nadir. The number of active professional steel guitarists was small, and their median age was high — in other words, there were very few younger players emerging. The sales of both steel-guitar records and instruments were inconsequential.

Even when Hawaiian music began to experience a local revival in the early 1970s, it was not the steel but the slack-key guitar that led the way. Just as the steel once had its day, the slack-key was to have its own measure of popularity.

Nevertheless, interest in steel guitar has begun to grow with the general revitalization of Hawaiian music. This resurgence has been due partly to the efforts of The Hawaiian Music Foundation through its concerts — especially its historic all-steel concert in 1973 and its *Halau* [a school with traditional connotations] with classes in steel guitar.

–Donald D. Kilolani and George S. Kanahele

[Although there is a small grassroots resurgence of steel in Hawaii, it would still take a visitor a great deal of effort to find a band that features steel even in a minor role. On the mainland, related Dobro and pedal-steel styles are quite popular in country and bluegrass, and reissues of old steel-guitar records have appeared. Hopefully these reissues and even this book will rekindle interest.]

Characteristics of Hawaiian-Style Steel Guitar

The trait most associated with steel guitar is the glissando, an easy effect even for beginners, but a difficult one to really master. It is this technique that enables the instrument to imitate some of the nuances of the human voice. Sliding between notes is so obvious that it is often overused, resulting in the infamous "Ha-whiney" guitar.

You should be aware of a few different approaches to the slide:

A. Start sliding to the desired note as soon as you pick. In this way the pitch at the beginning of the slide has no duration. You get a slide sound and one distinct note.

B. Pick a note, hold it, and then slide to a second note without picking the latter — two notes and one pick.

C. Repeat B, but pick the note at the end of the slide — a pick-slide-pick.

These slur varieties may be obvious, but they are the kind of differences that define distinctive styles. The tablature symbols for these slides are, respectively:

These symbols are discussed further in the chapter on "Reading Tablature."

There are other parameters involved: the speed of a glissando, its length, and the notes on which you choose to use a sliding attack.

In the early days of Hawaiian guitar, players contrasted slides with bursts of staccato notes. Nowadays an all-legato approach is by far the most popular. In Jerry Byrd, the leading stylist of the past 20 years, it is realized to an extreme. To achieve uninterrupted legato phrasing, it is necessary to move the bar horizontally; i.e., along the strings, rather than vertically across them. So,

would be preferable to

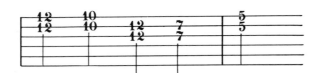

There is a specific application of staccato attack generic to Hawaiian steel. It usually involves picking a short note on an open (usually the first) string, and then one on the same string at least 4 frets higher (sometimes as many as 16 higher). This jump from low to high pitch is similar to (and is probably meant to imitate) the Hawaiian vocal yodel. The first note is sometimes played on a lower string, then immediately damped and the bar tilted to play a higher-pitched string. The lower note has been called a "hula note," but I prefer the more whimsical description "Hawaiian hiccup." This note is occasionally so staccato that I have tabbed it as a grace note; although, in context, it is usually easier to assign it a sixteenth- or eighth-note

duration. Some examples are pointed out in the text before each tune.

Sometimes the first note is held (i.e., not staccato) so the yodel effect is muted. See *"Kiho Alu"* for some examples.

Vibrato is another vocal-related effect that has become overwhelmingly prominent. There are some players who seem to keep it going continuously in every tune. This overkill has been contemptuously referred to as "steel player's palsy." Like sliding, any idiosyncrasy can be overdone, thus blunting its impact. Sometimes vibrato can be used as a blurring mask for out-of-tuneness. (Everyone is guilty of this at one time or another.) In moderation, vibrato can marginally extend the duration of a note which is decaying in volume. More importantly, it can add a hard-to-describe quality (often referred to as "warmth") to the tone of a note. I should mention that some Hawaiian singers also employ a marked vibrato at every opportunity.

Listen carefully to the vibrato of players you like. Try to imitate the width and speed of their bar oscillation. In slow to moderately paced tunes, the speed of many Hawaiian-style players approximates triplet timing and a width of about ½ fret to either side of the central note. For example, using the 5th fret as a reference, this might be tabbed as:

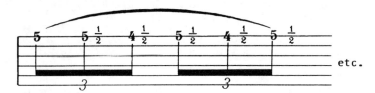

Remember, this is only a starting point for your own interpretation and is not meant to be played literally. Some guitarists' vibrato rates are faster or slower or variable, even in the middle of a passage.

Harmonics is the device most often used to vary a steel's tone. This may originally have been in imitation of falsetto singing. Frequent resorts to very high-pitched, artificial harmonics seems to be a favorite tactic of electric lap steelers.

Another voice-related effect is in mimicry of a low-pitched, guttural tone used in traditional chanting. To approximate the tone, pick the low strings quite close to he bridge and play relatively hard.

Steel-guitar tremolo is the quick alternating of notes on two (usually adjacent) strings. Although sometimes done as quickly as possible, a typical rate (like vibrato) is in triplet rhythm. For example, on the first and second strings, fret 5:

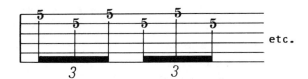

As with vibrato, everyone has a slightly different interpretation. When done in combination with a bar oscillation, the notes can lose their individual identities, and the trademark "crying" sound of the steel guitar emerges. Without the vibrato, tremolo can be used as a sustain device, especially for acoustic guitars.

Acoustic steelers sometimes use a "scrape" artifice for emphasis. This is usually accomplished by a quick, upward strum by the thumb, while simultaneously tilting the bar forward. So, as a string is hit, it is already being damped. If you time it just right and pick just as the bar is being lifted, you can achieve a metallic, almost snare-drum sound as the strings momentarily rattle against the bar. (See "Reading Tablature" for further information.)

An obvious harmonic embellishment is the addition of a harmony note. These double stops are often played in slant positions. The better players have control of both forward and reverse slants. To keep a legato sound, they opt for positions of varying degrees of difficulty rather than straight bars on other string combinations.

Hammer-ons and pull-offs are used much less frequently than in bluegrass music, where an acoustic steel (always a resophonic guitar) is often capoed up the neck to increase the opportunity to use this technique.

A peripherally related subject is the choice of bar. The oldest commercially made types were flat and thin. These models were succeeded by cylindrical "bullet" bars of varying lengths and diameters that are still favored by electric lap and pedal steelers. The added weight gives more tone and sustain, while the rounded shape makes vibrato and slants a bit easier.

Nowadays most acoustic players favor the "Stevens"-type bar (named after the original producer of the shape). This is basically a cylinder with indentations on the top and sides for easier gripping. The severely angled edges of this type of bar make pull-offs easier than do the rounded edges of the bullet shape.

No particular picking patterns are favored. Your right hand follows the dictates of the melodic line. Occasionally, three-finger "forward rolls" are employed, especially in some of the older tunes. Usually associated with bluegrass, the form of the forward roll is a series of thumb-index-middle-thumb-index-middle, etc., picking. These can be on separate strings as in **"Indiana March"** and **"Hilo March"** or on one string as in *"Tomi Tomi #1,"* **"Hula Blues #2,"** and **"Hula Blues #3."** If the tempo of the tune is moderate, it is sometimes possible to do a one-string roll with just thumb and index or middle.

Even in the earliest recordings, Hawaiian guitarists exhibited the influence of the then-current pop styles of the United States. In the timing and choice of notes, evidence of ragtime, early jazz, and, to a lesser extent, blues is clear. It is possible that some of the syncopation may have derived, in part, from Spanish, Portuguese, or Mexican visitors. Of course, America and the former three nations have an African musical connection. Notes held across bar lines or the second beat of measures are typical ragtime melodic rhythms. It is also possible that ties between the second upbeat and the third downbeat of a measure may be traceable to the pre-contact *mele.*

Occasionally I will mention that a piece should be played with swing eighths, the kind of

Cover of a 1934 steel-guitar book published by Wm. J. Smith Company, New York City (courtesy of Phil Zimmerman)

timing associated with the jazz of the late 1920s and 1930s. This indicates that the eighth notes should not be timed evenly. To get a swing feeling, the actual timing is more like tied triplets; i.e., the first note is held for ⅔ of a beat and the second for the remaining ⅓. Listen carefully for this type of phrasing on your Hawaiian records. All players express it slightly differently in different circumstances. It is easier to hear than to describe. (See "Reading Tablature" for additional information.)

The Hawaiian-style steel guitarists who made their professional careers in the continental United States picked up tricks that were crowd pleasers in their day. Such vaudevillian "shtick" as quickly dragging the bar along the frets (easiest with a bullet bar), beating the resonator cover with picks, and scraping the metal sound-hole mesh to produce washboard-like sounds are machinations that lurk in the dark corners of this music. Cheap theatrics? Sure! Lots of fun? Sure! One example is produced in **"Honolulu Bound #1."** Let your id be your guide.

Electric players have their own tricks — employing pseudo-wah-wah effects by sliding while diddling with tone or volume controls, or picking with the volume off and sliding while swelling the volume. Then there are the laughter imitations, cartoon sound effects, train and plane noises — all fodder for the idle mind. Benny Nawahi, Sol Hoopii, Roy Smeck, and Alvino Rey are all great players who have occasionally resorted to such tomfoolery.

Another signature of Hawaiian music is a one- or two-measure turnaround or vamp that usually involves a V chord to I chord progression; e.g., in the key of C, a G7 to C; or in B♭, an F7 to B♭. These musical afterthoughts are tacked on the end of a stanza almost like the "amen" response of a congregation. In fact, they may be derived from the chordal cadence in the choral hymn singing taught in Hawaii during the mid-19th century. They are best defined by some examples. In the key of G, the Hawaiian vamp would typically be:

Sometimes they are strung together with added chords. These turnarounds are indicated

in the first few tunes in this book, but you will soon be able to recognize them.

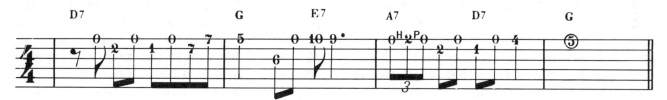

The original slack-key-derived major tuning of Hawaiian guitars is not conducive to playing embellished major and minor chords. Two ways to get at least part of the chords (without retuning) are by pulling the strings behind the bar to raise their pitch, and by using the **width** of the bar to cover two strings. Bob Brozman calls the latter "fudging." It usually needs a dose of vibrato to disguise a bit of out-of-tuneness. String pulling is more demanding but, in the long run, more dependable and versatile. (See *The Dobro Book* and *The Dobro Chord*

Book for a more complete exposition of this technique.) There are several opportunities to use these skills scattered through this book.

To avoid pulling and fudging, there has been a seemingly incessant experimentation with all manner of tunings. It seems that almost everyone has a string or two that they set up differently: A major, G major, low bass and high bass, E major, E7, C♯m, C♯m7, A6, C6, F♯9, B11, E13 . . . help, I'm going *pupule!*

Special Hawaiian Effects

Perhaps one of the most common effects employed by some of the best Hawaiian players, aside from the exaggerated and unmusical whine caused by the ever present slide, is the little variation introduced into many melodies by interpolating the open E string between the melody notes played on this string. This is usually done when playing in the key of A, since the open E string then fits in with both the A and E chords belonging to this key. These open string notes sound much like grace notes, and if actually printed in the music, would appear like the lower lines of the following Example.

Variations of this sort should be used with great discretion, since they have the effect of "jazzing" the melody, and this can be carried to undesirable extremes. The same may also be said of the exaggerated use of the grace notes and slides, which might even cause some unsophisticated person to mistake the *Hawaiian* guitar for the "whine" guitar!

A warning to steelers from *Stahl's New Hawaiian Guitar Method*, published by William C. Stahl, Milwaukee, Wisconsin ca. 1927

This welter of permutations littering the history of steel guitar is a matter of concern for all students of the genre. Should you buy a double-necked steel? A triple- or quadruple-neck and each with a different tuning? How about a six- or eight-string lap steel or even a single- or double-necked pedal steel? With 10 or 12 strings, in E13 or C6? Too many choices!

G major is now the standard tuning for acoustic steel players. Since most of the early stuff was recorded in this or the related A major, the majority of tunes in this book use G. If you prefer A tuning, you can play the tablature in this book as written, then just read the accompanying chords one whole step (2 frets) higher. For example, in G tuning the 10th fret gives an F chord; in A tuning the same fret makes a G chord.

I have tabbed a few numbers in some of the favorite retunings and then employed a lower-pitched version of them, since it is easier to slack the strings than to change to thinner-gauged strings or to own more than one guitar. If you already have an instrument tuned to the higher versions, again play the tablature as written and transpose the chord accompaniment. A more thorough explanation of this and related enigmas can be found in "Retunings."

With all the possibilities, it can be a real hardship to determine the tuning used on a particular recording. Most players since the mid-1930s have recorded with at least two variations. After you have played extensively in a particular tuning, you can recognize certain note sequences which tend to show up frequently. With luck, some of these will show up on the record you are studying. Without the experience, it is almost impossible to differentiate (sorry). However, you can play almost exactly the same riffs in related tunings. As the Hawaiians say, it is

"he nane huna ia."

"a riddle whose answer is well hidden."

One of the defining attributes of a particular player's style is the way he or she chooses to fret a series of notes. Any note can be sounded on different strings and frets, with each possibility having a different timbre and suggesting different slides and staccato phrasing. For example, here are four barrings of the same lick in measure 2 of **"Cunha Medley:"**

The first version is the most obvious and probably the way Pale K. Lua played it. It gives either a slide-y sound as the bar moves horizon-tally or a staccato effect with each note immediately damped, as on this old recording.

The above example allows for a less staccato approach while still avoiding slides. There is also opportunity for a pull-off. The last two examples, utilizing no open strings, allow marginally more even timbre on each note:

Distinguishing between these fretting variations is a most difficult task, so feel free to experiment with alternatives to my preferences. My choices were based on aural evidence and what seemed to be the easiest possibility.

All this detailed description can serve as a guide to what to listen for on Hawaiian-guitar recordings and how to construct your own solos. It is also a case study of how an instrument's character — both advantages and seeming shortcomings — can be used to conform to a distinct style of music.

Special Hawaiian Stage Effects

Many professional Hawaiian Guitarists, especially those native to Hawaii, make their playing especially interesting and effective by the use of original tricks and effects. Several of the most useful are explained herewith.

Tremolo Glissando

As the steel slides at moderate speed from a low to a high note or from a high note to one lower, tremolo as rapidly as possible on the 1st string with the thumb and 1st finger. In the following example slide the steel slowly enough so that two counts are occupied by the slide. The effect is of a quarter or eighth tone chromatic glissando. This effect may also be played on the slide trombone but is not so effective.

Bird Imitation

Use 1st string. Place steel 3 or 4 inches from the bridge, pick the string firmly with left hand finger and as string is picked slide steel rapidly almost up to bridge. Return steel to first position and repeat rapidly. A little practice will enable the player to make this sound like the chirping of a bird. No attention need be given to any particular pitch.

The Chicken

Place 4th finger of left hand firmly on 1st string at 10th fret and pick 1st string with right hand, immediately drop steel on 1st string at 12th fret and pick string again in the usual way, pick string again with steel at 12th fret and instantly slide to 13th fret. These three notes should be sounded in the rhythm of a chicken's cackle. Study the example below.

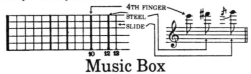

Music Box

Press the strings to fingerboard with palm edge of left hand and draw thumb-pick back and forth across strings in arpeggio fashion. This will give the effect of winding up a music box spring. Study the example.

Steel Novelty

Play any solo as usual, except that the palm edge of the right hand is to rest very lightly on the strings, but so as not to interfere with using the thumb and finger picks as usual. Use very little pressure so that the pitch of the tones is definite.

Flageolet, Bell or Chime

These flute-like tones are produced by playing harmonics. Place the steel on the strings in the usual way, then touch the point of right hand 4th finger to the strings 12 frets higher than where the steel touches the string. Turn the right hand so that it is possible to use the thumb pick between the 4th finger and the bridge. Pick the string and lift 4th finger from string at the same instant. What are known as palm harmonics may also be used. These are produced by placing the edge of the right hand palm over the fret for the harmonic wanted so it touches the strings, and picking the string or strings with the thumb pick at the same time lifting the hand from the string. Harmonics are produced this way at the 12th, 7th, or 5th fret above the steel or the fingerboard nut.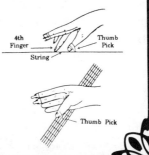

Curious byways of Hawaiian-guitar technique quoted from Volume 3 of the *Nick Lucas Hawaiian Guitar Method* published by Nicomede Music Co., Altoona, Pennsylvania, 1940 (courtesy of George Youngblood)

Reading Tablature

I have combined standard rhythm notation and guitar tablature with some special steel-guitar symbols to convey basic musical information about the tunes that follow. This music is not meant to be sight read. Take it very slowly, and be sure you play the rhythm correctly. Count out the beats of each measure, if necessary.

Each of the six lines of the tablature represents a string, with the thinnest, highest-pitched string on top and the thickest, lowest-pitched string at the bottom. It is just like looking down at your guitar in playing position. A number on a line indicates which fret of that string should be picked, so

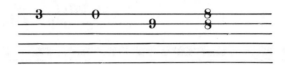

means that you should first pick string 1, fret 3, then first string, open, string 2, fret 9, and finally strings 1 and 2, fret 8, simultaneously.

To indicate how long you should hold each note, stems, flags, and beams are attached to the fret number to symbolize the number of beats (or foot taps). The time signature at the beginning of

each piece tells you its beat structure. The bottom number of 4/4 notation means that a quarter note is one beat long. The top number tells you how many beats there are per measure. In the above example, there are four quarter notes (or beats or foot taps) per measure. 2/4 means there are only two quarter notes per measure. When you see

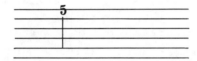

in a music text, hold that note for the time it takes you to tap your foot once, from foot-on-floor until just before your foot taps again. The attached stem indicates one quarter note. A circle around a fret number with a stem attached means the

note is held for two beats (as long as the bottom number in the time signature is 4, which is the case for all the tunes in this book). A four-beat whole note is encircled but has no stem.

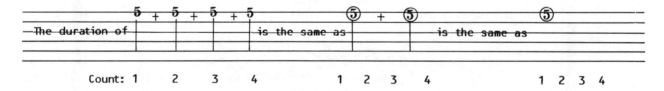

In the first grouping, the 5th fret is picked four times; in the second, twice, with each note held twice as long; and, in the last, just once. Whether the beam is up or down has no effect on the count.

A quarter note can be divided into two eighth notes, one when the foot is on the floor

(sometimes called the downbeat or strong beat), and the other when the foot is in the air. The latter is called the offbeat, upbeat, or just "and." Beams and flags are attached to the stems to indicate durations shorter than a quarter note. When there is a series of short notes, the flags are usually joined to form a beam.

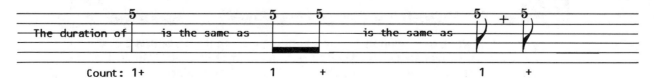

Eighths can be broken down into sixteenths, symbolized by a second flag or beam.

When a note is dotted, lengthen its duration by half of its original value.

A second dot means to additionally add a quarter of the note's original value.

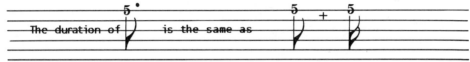

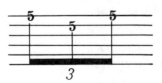

This is a quarter-note triplet. It means to play three evenly spaced notes in the space of one quarter note. The first is played on the downbeat; the second, just before the upbeat; and the third, just after.

In the following tied-triplet notation, the first note is held for ⅔ of a beat, and the second for ⅓. This phrasing is used in swing rhythm.

This is an eighth-note triplet, with the three notes played in the space of a half beat:

This is a half-note triplet, with the notes evenly dividing two beats:

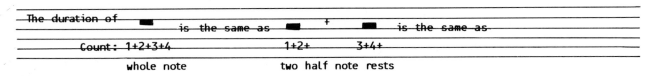

Rests have their own symbols and are counted similarly:

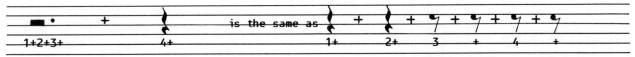

A suggested tempo for each tune is mentioned in its introduction, so MM = 100 means to set your metronome to that speed.

In just a bit, some of the trickier tablatures in this book will be deciphered for practice, so you can face the music with confidence. First, here are some other symbols with which you may not be familiar. There is no need for memorization, just refer back here when you meet a stranger. In fact, when you first work out a piece, ignore all markings except string, fret, and duration. Slowly add the requisite slides and embellishments after you have a basic idea of the melody. All this is immeasurably easier if you have a recorded copy of the tune.

A. Slide to the indicated note. This is usually a quick glissando of 1 fret or less:

B. Slide down or up after the note:

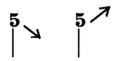

C. The slur sign in this context means to pick the first note, then slide to the next, but do not pick the second note:

24

D. The horizontal legato sign under the slur means to slide to that fret and then pick that note as soon as it is reached. Sometimes this sign is omitted to avoid excess notation clutter. In context, my intent will be obvious. When a tune is filled with this kind of phrasing, I will use it a few times and then leave it to your discretion to continue with the right feel. Of course, you should be prepared to rearrange any tablature to suit your own taste.

E. The tie sign is identical to the slur, but it only extends the duration of a note. Here the 5th fret is held for five beats:

Depending on context, a similar situation might be notated:

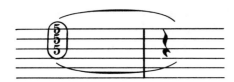

F. The staccato symbol placed over a note means to damp the sound and leave an audible space between the notes.

The actual rhythm might be:

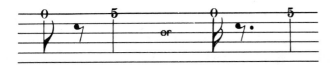

G. A grace note is held for as short a time as possible and is not included in the count of time duration of a measure. What little time it does use is ordinarily borrowed from the preceding note:

H. "n.h." or a degree sign (°) is the abbreviation for natural harmonics, fretted with the edge of your left hand, not the bar.

I. "a.h." or a diamond sign (◊) is the symbol for artificial harmonics, fretted with the bar and 12 frets higher by the palm of your right hand. (See *The Dobro Book* for a complete explanation of this technique and others with which you might be unfamiliar.)

J. The notation below means to quickly strum anywhere from four to six strings and hold the strum for a quarter note.

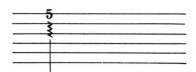

K. The following indicates a "scrape." Quickly strum the strings, but block each one as soon as it is picked. The only one that should be left sounding in this example is string 1, fret 5, for a quarter note. The "x" marks the highest string that should be damped. Sometimes the scrape is done as a grace note (e.g., **"Honolulu Bound,"** measures 52 and 57) or slowly enough to have a duration of its own (as in measures 8 and 12 of the same tune).

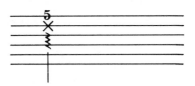

L. Parentheses around a fret number indicate a "ghost" note that is almost swallowed amid the welter of its fellows. It also can indicate the approximate pitch on selected beats during an extended slide, as in *"Tomi Tomi."*

M. An asterisk means that you should either pull the second string behind the bar to bring it up to the pitch of the 5th fret, or use the width of the bar to fret both the first and second strings at the 5th fret. Most bars are wide enough to easily cover the distance between adjacent strings.

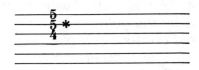

N. The arrow as used in **"La Rosita"** means to pull the first string behind the bar so that its pitch is raised to that of the 14th fret even though the bar is on fret 13:

O. The double arrow, as in *"Na Lei O Hawaii,"* means to raise the pitch of the indicated note 2 frets so that, here, it gives the note of the 12th fret:

P. "H" means to pick the indicated open string, then hammer on to the 2nd fret of the *same* string — one pick and two notes:

Q. "P" means to sound the open string by pulling off the bar after picking the first note — again, one pick and two notes:

R. This sign over a particular fret number means to accent that note:

>

S. "T," "M," or "I" underneath the tablature lines indicate suggested fingerings for a lick. T = thumb, M = middle finger, and I = index finger.

T. Roman numerals over the tablature indicate the beginning of a different section of the tune:

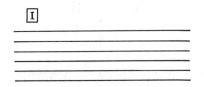

U. Measure numbers are placed at the lower left of each tablature line. Lead-in notes are not counted as a measure. Chords are notated over the tab.

V. Tunings other than the standard G are notated at the beginning of a piece.

Here are some examples of tablature counted out, with the ornaments explained. These samples should give any tablature-reading tyros confidence to tackle anything in this book.

1. Here is measure 1 of *"Mai Poina Oe Iau:"*

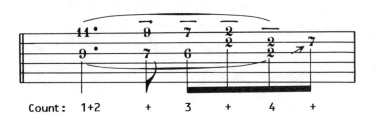

Count: 1+2   +   3   +   4   +

Start in slant position, then slide to and pick the 9/7 double stop of the offbeat after the second foot tap. Slide to and then pick 7/6, then slide and straighten the bar as soon as you reach the 2nd fret on the offbeat after the third beat. Do not damp the string until after the count of four, then immediately slide on only the second string using the tip of the bar.

2. Here is measure 1 of **"Cunha Medley:"**

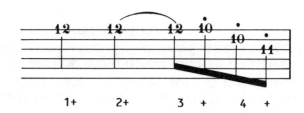

Hold the second note for 1½ beats, then play the last three notes staccato.

3. Here are measures 10–12 of *"Hue Hue."* This tune is in 2/4 meter:

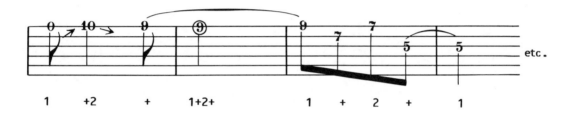

Slide up to and down from string 1, fret 10, then pick and hold string 1, fret 9, from the offbeat of 2, through the two beats of the next measure and the first eighth note of measure 12.

The last note of the 12th measure is tied to the next measure.

4. Here are measures 8–10 of **"Hula Medley #2:"**

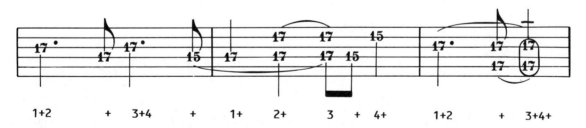

At the end of measure 8, slide from fret 15 to 17 with the bar flat on the strings. Keep the fourth string ringing, and pick the second string on the second beat of measure 9. Block both strings after the third downbeat. In the last mea-sure, let string 3 sound for the whole measure, but pick the string on the first and third beats. The fourth string is picked on the "and" after the second beat.

Many of these tunes feature lots of fast sixteenth-note picking. Syncopated series of sixteenth notes are much more difficult to read than similar groups of eighth notes. I use "cut-time" convention (¢) to take a 2/4-meter tune and double the duration of every note, so that the relative durations are still the same. For example:

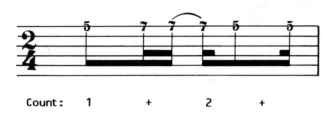

is equivalent to:

This time signature just slows everything down for ease of reading.

Believe it or not, I think we are ready to play some music.

"Ua ahu ka imu, e lawalu ku i'a."

"The oven is ready, let the fish be cooked."

Wahio Wale Kahilo
"The Ancients Exposed"

The chapter title refers to the revealing of old secrets. Here are some old, short tunes that reveal some basic truths about Hawaiian music. The explanations in this chapter are more detailed than in the following sections.

These are some of the prettiest and most popular Island tunes, so do not snub them just because they are presented with a minimum of ostentation.

Let's begin with a 19th-century composition, *"Hanohano-E,"* which means something like "give honor."

Do not block the strings (allowing note overlap) until the end of measure 4. You have to move quickly to reach the correct location for the artificial harmonics in measures 2, 4, 8, and 9. These harmonics are "fills" to add interest while the melody is stationary.

Watch for the reverse slant in measure 6. There are many more of these to come, and this will be your only warning.

Play measure 7 with the tip of the bar, touching only the indicated string. All other measures are played with the bar flat. An alternate fretting for measure 7 is:

The tempo should be about MM = 110–120, but only after you have worked the tune up slowly.

TAPE #048

HANOHANO -E

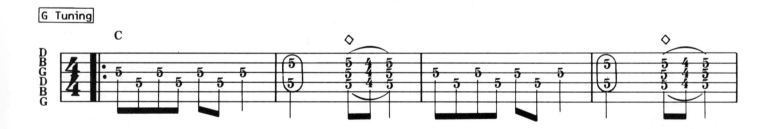

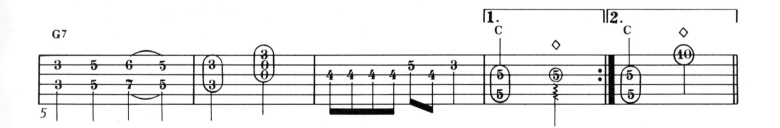

29

The next appetizer in our *luau* is a straight-ahead arrangement of a pretty melody called *"Moani Ke Ala."* It is played entirely with first- and third-string slants, with typical grace notes and slides appended to enliven the proceedings.

First learn to play it ignoring all the spaghetti hanging off the notes. At first glance, all these "slide-and-pick" legato symbols may be daunting. After I do this for a few tunes, you will get the idea of where to place this type of phrasing, and then some of the interpretation will be left to you.

Play this piece at about MM = 84. A recording of *"Moani Ke Ala"* can be heard on *Original Hawaiian Classics* (Folkways 8714) played by Tony Ku, a Chinese aficionado of old tunes. The title has something to do with a gently wafted fragrance, a truly Polynesian concept.

MOANI KE ALA

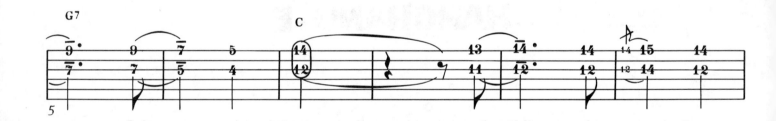

"Pupu O 'Ewa" is one of Hawaii's best-known melodies under its English title **"Pearly Shells."** The title means "shells of Ewa," an old sugar plantation town on Oahu. Its composer is unknown, but it was supposedly written as part of a campaign to raise money for the construction of a church during the reign of King Kalakaua.

This is another example of the stylistic predilection for double stops, especially on slow tunes. Play this at about MM = 60. Again, ignore grace notes, slurs, and slides until you have a firm grasp of the melody.

This rendition is tabbed to minimize slants and to familiarize you with some second/fourth-string and third/fifth-string combinations. Most players prefer to play slow tunes on the top three strings because of the greater sustain, but be aware that there is always at least one alternative fretting for every double stop. Exploring these possibilities is a good way to learn your way around the fretboard. You may find a substitute more to your liking.

As in *"Moani Ke Ala,"* the grace notes are not damped, but are kept ringing as parts of double stops.

When sliding in measure 6, pull the bar off the second string as you approach fret 14. Damp that string immediately so that it does not vibrate during the rest of the slide.

Strum slowly in measure 7, giving an arpeggio. For most acoustic guitars the 21st fret is off the neck. You will have to look for landmarks other than frets such as scratches, various sound holes, and screens.

After you have learned this tune with the picks and slides as shown, experiment with other combinations. You are the final arbiter of taste. Just be sure that you adjust your slides to arrive at the next note exactly on time; otherwise, your playing will sound queasy.

This interpretation of *"Pupu O 'Ewa"* is based on the playing of Tony Ku.

"Alahula Pu'uloa,
he ala hele no Ka'ahupahau"

"In the seas of Pearl Harbor,
the path trod by Ka'ahupahau"
(the shark goddess who protects Pearl Harbor)

PUPU O 'EWA

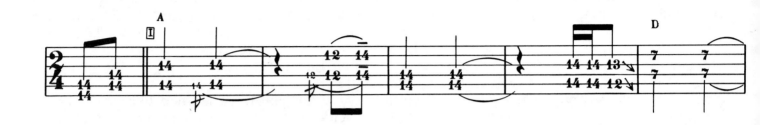

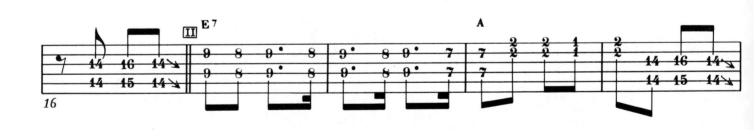

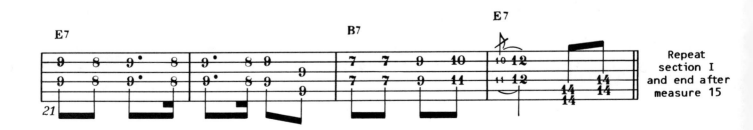

Repeat
section I
and end after
measure 15

"Sweet *Lei Lehua*" was written by King Kalakaua, who reigned from 1874 to 1891, the next-to-last Hawaiian monarch. The *lehua* is a tree with gaudy red and orange blossoms, and this is one of several tunes with this title. Play it at MM = 80 or a bit faster.

The tablature begins with a hackneyed two-measure Hawaiian turnaround or vamp and ends with a double-dipper (the last four measures). The latter has an extended chord progression. Let the open strings ring.

Between the introduction and exit is an example of the simple, uncluttered essence of beautiful Hawaiian music.

SWEET LEI LEHUA

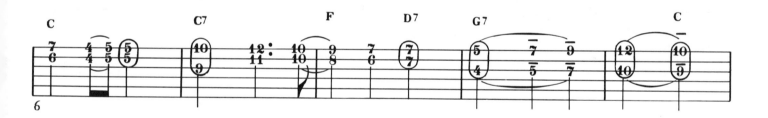

"Mai Poina Oe Ia'u" (loosely translated as "forget me not") should be played quite slowly, at about MM = 60. This leaves sufficient time to contemplate a serious vibrato. When playing the repeat, vary the arrangement with some tremolos and/or artificial harmonics. Any adjacent-string double stops are good candidates for the latter.

Measures 5 and 6 should be phrased like measures 1 and 2, but some of the symbol clutter has been removed — you are being weaned of some legato notation. In measures 1 and 5, the slide to string 2, fret 7, should be short (not all the way from the 2nd fret) and fast. You might like to harmonize this note with string 3, fret 6.

In the second measure, block string 5, fret 9, after 1½ beats by tilting the bar forward. Meanwhile, keep the third string sounding as you slide and then pick string 3, fret 8. Then place the bar flat again for the last double stop of the measure.

Finally, measure 10 features one of my favorite little Hawaiian flourishes, a I-♭VI-I chord turnaround, here A-F-A. Start the slide to fret 14 on the last beat of measure 10. Try this lick as an artificial harmonic. Aah, *palekaiko momona* (sweet paradise).

This tune can be heard on *Guitare Hawaienne Authentique* (Playasound 65027).

MAI POINA OE IA'U

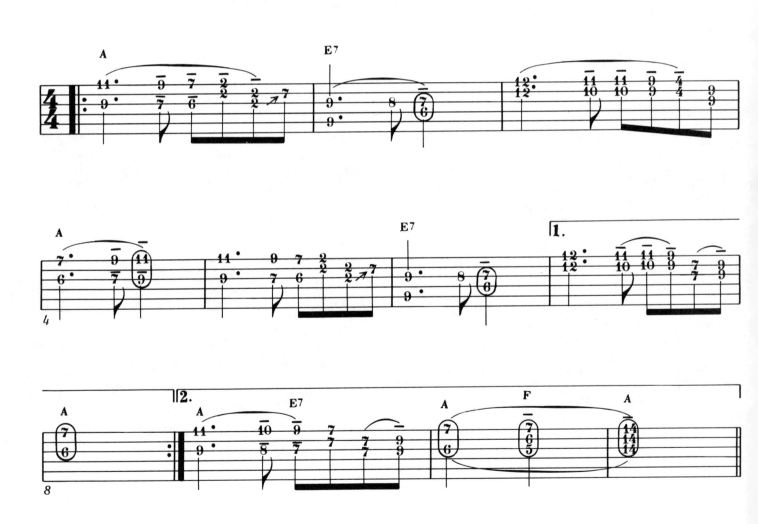

This version of *"Lehua"* is based on the stalwart stylings of Sol Hoopii, the big *kahuna* of the classic period of steel guitar. He had his guitar in A tuning and played this in the key of G. Using the same fretting as Hoopii, that transposes to the key of F in G tuning.

Hoopii uses some open strings to play a couple of hammer-on and pull-off triplets. In measure 2, the E note (string 1, fret 2) against a B♭ chord is an unexpected but piquant tone. Nice going, Sol. At the end of this measure, the third string, 5th fret, is used as a Hawaiian hiccup in imitation of a voice breaking, leaping up to string 1, fret 7.

Measure 6 is robbed of two beats (at least to the ears of someone accustomed to Western melodies). As usual, slowly count the number of beats and rhythm, and any confusion should clear like an early morning fog on Maui. (Is there any fog on Maui?)

Finally, the last two measures are another Hawaiian vamp with its last note (string 2, fret 6) typically anticipated by an eighth note. The last three notes are a tag, a musical afterthought.

Play *"Lehua"* at an unhurried pace, about MM = 116, being sure to give each note its full value and using vibrato on any note with a duration longer than a quarter note. A version of this piece can be heard on *Vintage Hawaiian Music — The Great Singers* (Rounder 1053).

Besides being a flower of the *'ohia* tree, *Lehua* is a place name on Niihau, a privately owned island in the Hawaiian archipelago.

Solomon Kaaiai Hoopii (1902–1953) was part of the second wave of Hawaiian musicians to seek their fortunes on the mainland. One of 21 children, he stowed away on a West Coast-bound liner (probably seeking some peace and quiet). He returned to his homeland only briefly and, as a result, is better known in the continental United States.

LEHUA

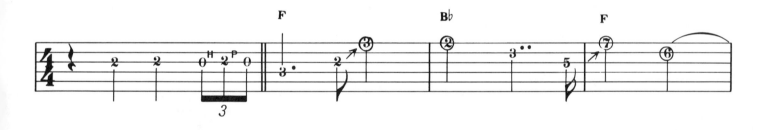

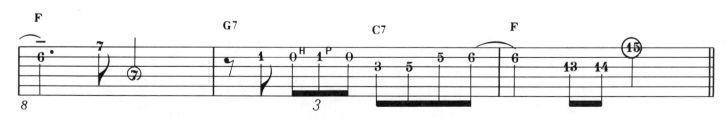

This version of *"Pauoha"* is based on the third part of Bob Brozman's **"Hawaiian Heat Waves Medley"** *(Hello Central... Give Me Dr. Jazz* on Rounder 3086). The simple melody is instantly recognizable as Hawaiian. Check out the motif in measures 3–4 and the turnaround in measure 10. The latter requires either a slant with a pull of the second string or a "fudge" slant using the width of the bar to cover strings 1 and 2.

Play this with the tip of the bar until measure 10. The seventh measure seems to be extra and can be omitted without detracting from the integrity of the tune.

The last three notes are again a tag. Play this at a cut-time tempo of *MM* = 140.

PAUOHA

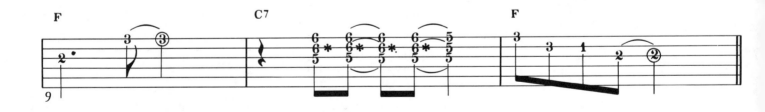

Ho'i Ana I Ke Kumu
"Back to the Source"

Let's go back to the source for a potpourri of ancient hulas arranged in *hula kui* style by some of the best first-generation steel guitarists.

Some of the obvious stylistic elements include the typical "hiccupping" yodel using open strings, staccato phrasing, playing along a string (as opposed to across several strings) while playing staccato, the linking of short phrases and tunes into a medley, and single-note picking (as opposed to double stops).

The **"Cunha Medley"** is based on the playing of an early master of steel guitar, Pale K. Lau. It is a typical arrangement of old hulas in *hula kui* style. Technique was archaic in the pre-resophonic, pre-electric days. His vibrato is narrower and quicker than that which became in vogue by 1930. Use the tip of the bar almost exclusively.

The first eight measures are an introduction taken from the last half of the full first section (measures 25–41). The first two sections have the sound of an old march, but the others are very hula. Play at a 2/4 meter of about MM = 95.

CUNHA MEDLEY

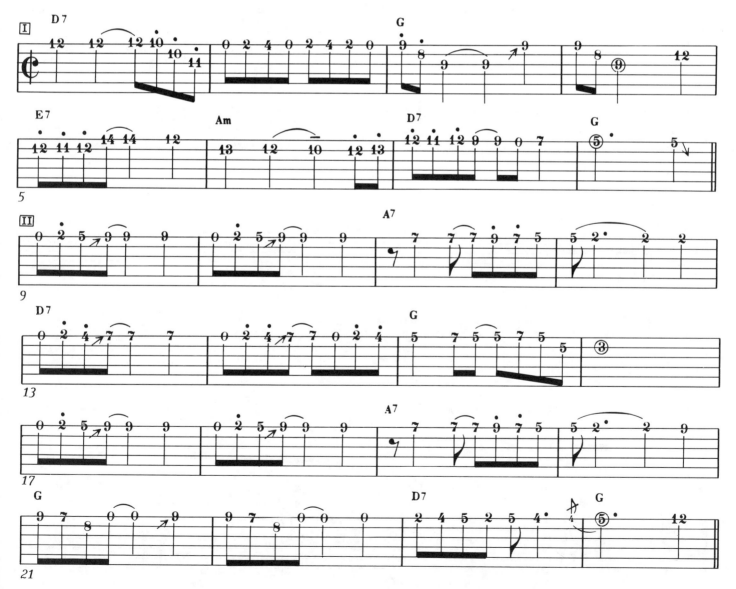

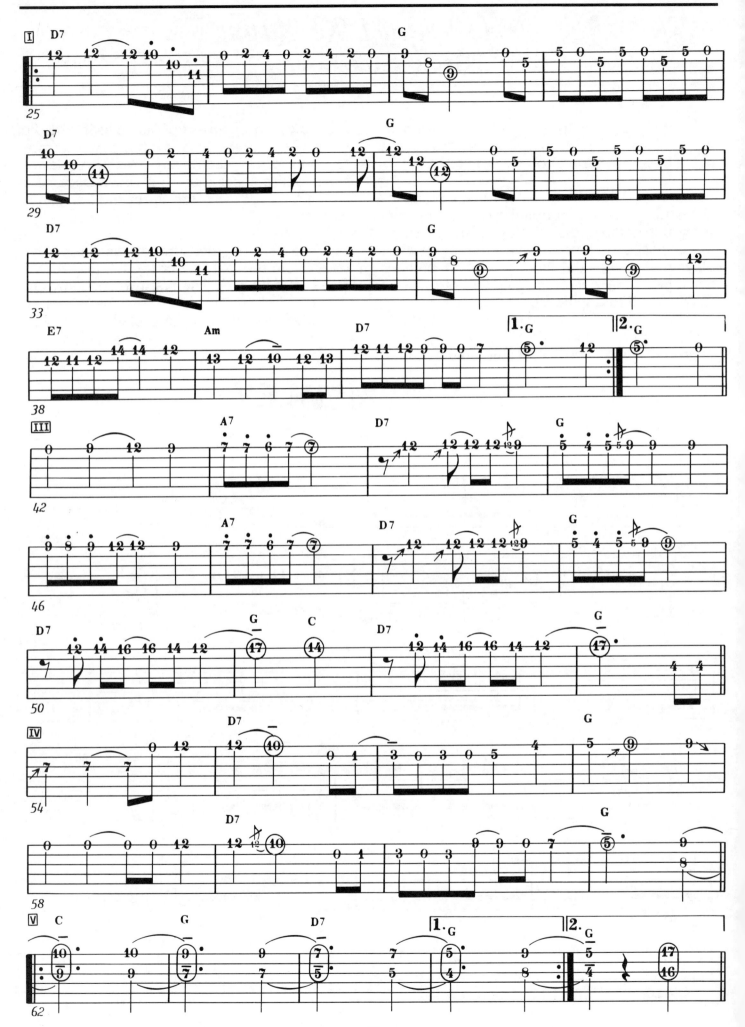

The march-like quality of parts of these early medley recordings must be due mostly to the influence of Henry Berger's Royal Hawaiian Band. The rollicking *"Kaui Kahio"* features an uncredited steel guitarist (who certainly sounds like Pale K. Lua) who plays it at a 2/4 tempo of about MM = 104.

As usual, the hiccupped notes on the open strings (e.g., the last notes of each of the first three measures) are held a little shorter than an eighth note. In measures 15, 16, and 45, the strums are on open strings except for string 1, fret 5, played with the tip of the bar.

The motif beginning in measure 22 is quoted again in section V of **"Cunha Medley"** and section II of *"Kaua I Ka Huahua'i."* An alternative form of measure 36 is:

A recording of *"Kaui Kahio"* can be found on *Hula Blues* (Rounder 1012).

KAUI KAHIO

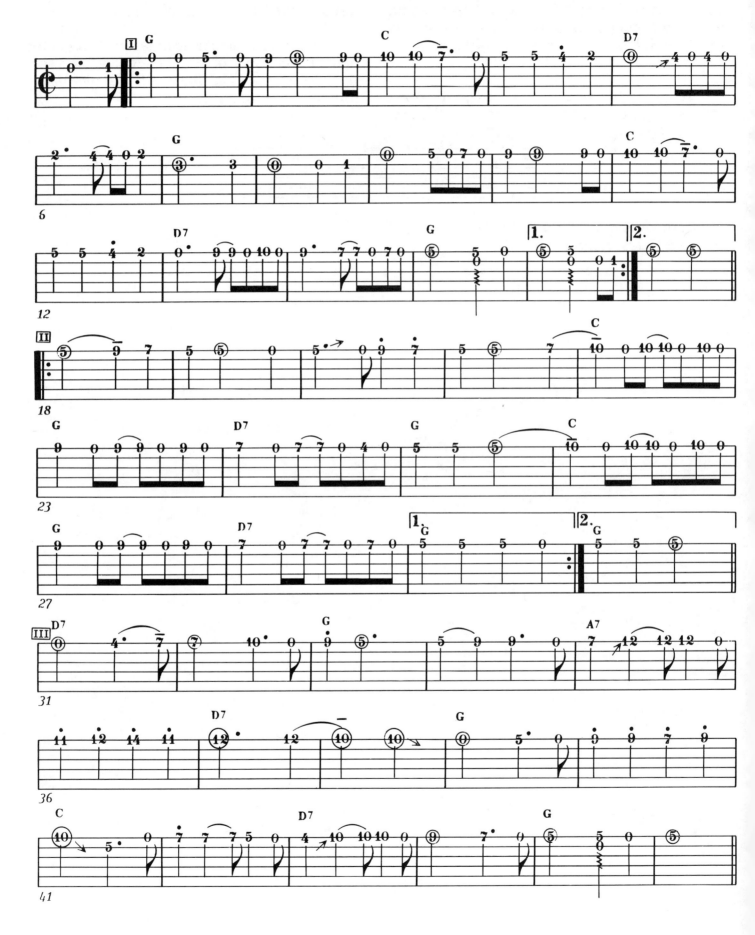

40

"*Hue Hue*" is a more mellow hula, played at about MM = 124. This arrangement is based on the playing of Sam Ku West, a man with as sweet a tricone vibrato as you could ever care to quiver your bar at. I use the sound of his velvet touch as a relaxant after a hard day of forging steel bars at the mill. His version can be heard on *Hawaiian Steel Guitar* (Folklyric 9009).

The last phrase of each verse (e.g., measures 12–15) is very turnaround-like and is followed by a true vamp. Check out the neat ways that West varies each verse's turnaround.

The slides in measures 14, 15, 26, etc., are about a fret long and so duplicate and blend into the following open first string. The licks in measures 18–19 and 38–39 are tags appended to turnarounds. It sounds like West actually played both as in measure 18, playing the same pitch consecutively but on two different strings; i.e., string 3, fret 4, and the open second string. But I like the sound as in measure 38.

Measure 41 heralds a beautifully constructed section, alternating straight picking with strummed and double-stopped natural harmonics. In the next verse, just before the end of measure 54, start the scrape on the 9th fret and slide as soon as the first string is picked. The thumb strum, finger pick, and slide happen serially but as close as possible to being simultaneous. The other scrapes in this tune are the usual kind, with no slides. The ties over the other grace-note scrapes are just indications of how closely tied the damped notes are to the main pitch.

Measure 56 ends with the grace note of a nice hiccup lick followed by a nasty fast slide between frets 17 and 12. The phrase in measures 62–65 is played with an insouciant nonchalance, each note reached barely in time but in a supremely unhurried fashion. The same lick is amplified in measures 82–85 and 124–127.

In the verse beginning in measure 95, the lower-register notes should be picked near the bridge to get a Hawaiian guttural tone. The thinner strings get "high end-y" when picked at the same place. The 98th measure can be played on the open third string, but the given fretting allows for vibrato.

Let as many notes as possible overlap in the last section, then end by repeating the first verse.

"*Hue hue*" refers to a double-time dance move that climaxes some hulas.

Sam Ku West (courtesy of Dirk Vogel)

HUE HUE

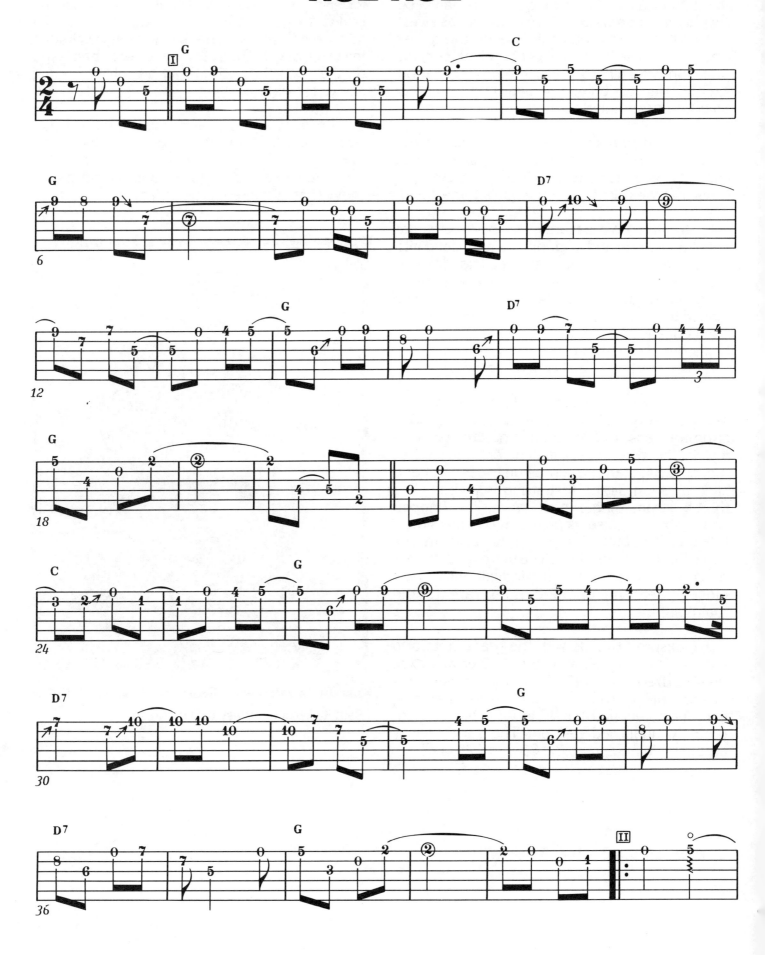

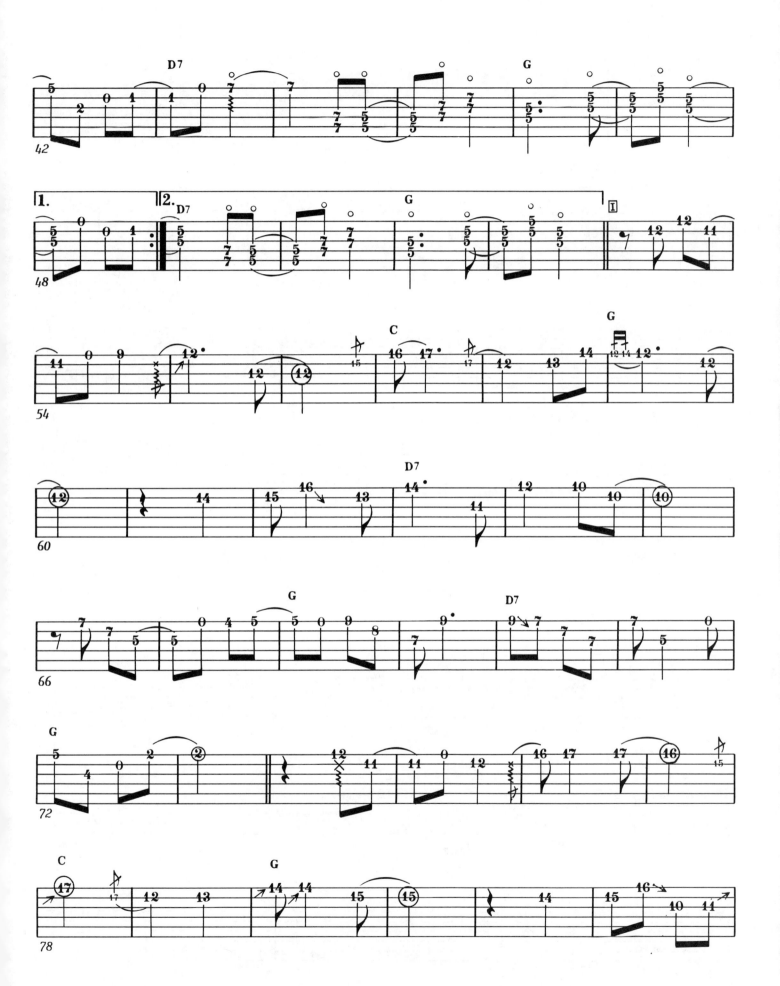

The elusive M. K. Moke calls his *"Hue Hue"* version **"Moana Chimes."** He has a flair for languorous, sluggish slides and vibrato. Of all the players I have heard, I feel that his simple yet subtle approach to the steel is truest to the pre-contact sound of Hawaiian *oles*. (Of course, I could be full of one-finger *poi*.)

Moke scatters artificial harmonics throughout his playing. The natural harmonic in measure 13 may be a mistake. Although it sounds fine, an artificial harmonic would be much easier. He plays the 12th fret artificially even though a natural harmonic would be easier, since the former allows vibrato.

The parentheses in measure 7 indicate the approximate pitch at the end of the slide. Although this is literally what he plays, the triplet in measure 31 might sound better as:

Attack **"Moana Chimes"** with cloying sweetness at MM = 90. A recording of this is on the reissue *Hawaiian Steel Guitar* (Folklyric 9009). The Moana Hotel was a luxury residence built in 1901.

MOANA CHIMES

"Paahana" has the same melody as the natural-harmonic section of Sam Ku West's *"Hue Hue."* It was recorded by the Moe family in 1929 under the ingenious alias of Madame Riviere's Hawaiians. Tau Moe played it at a brisk MM = 130 on *Vintage Hawaiian Music — The Great Singers* (Rounder 1053).

The parentheses in measure 4 indicate that the slide ends approximately at fret 5.

"Paahana" tells the story of a girl who flees to the forest to escape her evil stepmother.

*"Na'u i noho aku ia wao kele
la uka 'iu'iu Wahiawa."*

"I lived in the rain forests
The distant uplands of Wahiawa."

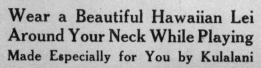

PAAHANA ♯ 1

This is another mix of old-sounding hulas based on a reading by Pale K. Lua. Section I has a march-like approach with plenty of open-string hiccups keeping the proceedings Hawaiian. Lua can be very staccato when he avoids slides as he goes up and down the first string.

Watch for the two-beat measure at bar 24. This same section has an added measure in the second ending. It seems twisted at first, but it has its own logic. I have removed some of these added and dropped beats from the tablature to ease reading.

In measures 34 and 44, start the slide immediately upon picking fret 21. After section V, repeat both III sections up to measure 49, then continue to section VI at measure 72.

This medley can be heard on *Hula Blues* (Rounder 1012). Play at about MM = 120.

HULA MEDLEY # 1

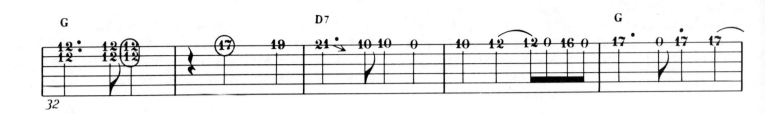

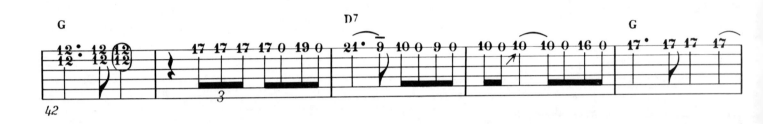

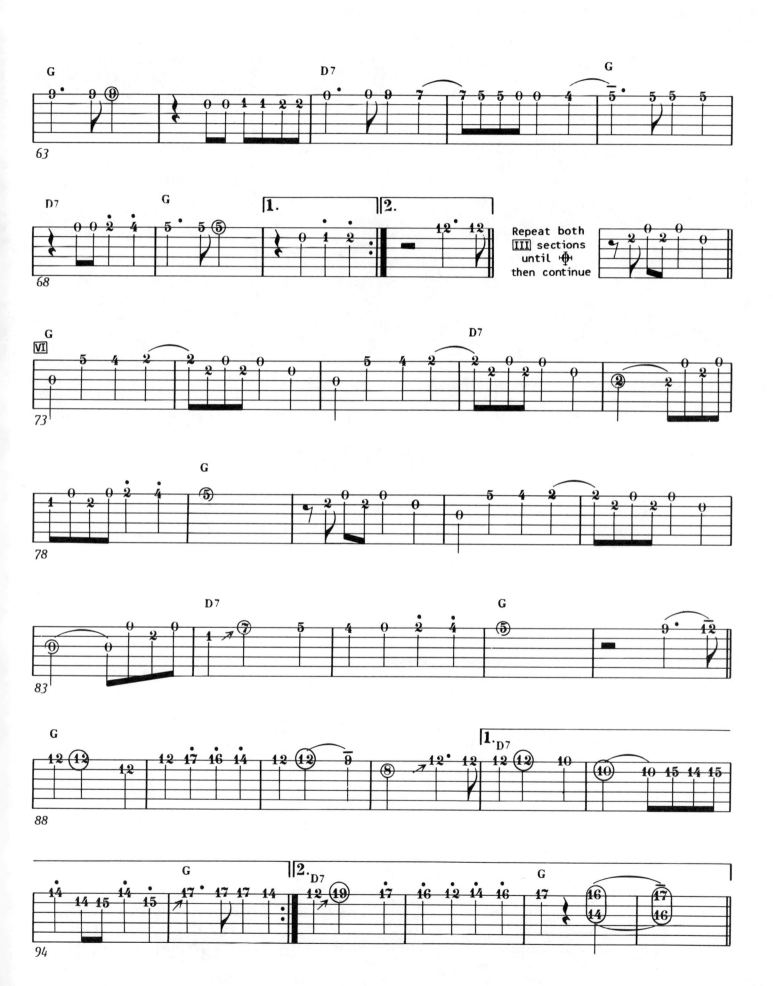

51

Kalama's Quartette is best known for its stirring vocal harmonies, but Mike Hanapi did some nice steel work on their hulas. These melodies are quite simple, but Hanapi's phrasing is very tricky, with the individual notes of some double stops having some independence. If necessary, write out the timing of each measure as illustrated in the "Reading Tablature" chapter.

You will find that the first section is just a few turnaround-like motives strung together with plenty of yodel-like leaps from string 4 to string 2.

This medley can be heard on *Kalama's Quartette—Early Hawaiian Classics* (Folklyric 9022). Play at a 2/4 tempo of about *MM* = 104.

Kalama's Quartette – back row (left to right): Bob Nawahine, William Kalama, Dan Pokipala; front: Mike Hanapi (courtesy of Bob Armstrong)

HULA MEDLEY ♯ 2

Harmonics *(ho'opapa)* are an obvious trick when dealing with a guitar tuned to an open chord. Although not a hula, **"Maui Chimes"** must be about as old as the concept of Hawaiian guitar.

This typical arrangement **("Maui Chimes #1")** opens with a hokey paraphrasing of **"Taps."** Let the notes overlap by letting the bar lie across all the strings. As a sop to some sort of musical esthetic, an expected note (string 1, fret 12) is given a twist by being played over an unexpected chord (E♭ in measure 7).

The tune itself begins with the introductory notes in measure 8, the only four notes in the entire arrangement not played as harmonics. The "etc." means to continue to play natural harmonics. There is no sliding with this technique, so your fretting fingers have to move quickly and exactly when changing frets.

The sixteenth-note triplets should be played as a forward roll. This actually is kind of a pleasant ditty based on an old American children's song, **"My Boat Is Sailing."**

After the melody, take advantage of the other frets that offer natural harmonics, the 4th (duplicated at the 9th) in the key of B, and the 7th in the key of D.

"Maui Chimes #1" is based on the playing of Hal Aloma.

Sol Hoopii's arrangement of this tune **("Maui Chimes #2")** has some neat variations. Watch for the extra barred note in measure 2. I have taken out some of his extra beats to make reading a bit easier.

Play between MM = 104–120. Among the many albums containing this tune are *Sol Hoopii — Volume One* (Rounder 1024), *A Musical Portrait of Hawaii* featuring Hal Aloma (Columbia CL 538), and *Hula Blues* (Rounder 1012).

Mother Lode of Portland, Oregon; Kathleen Fallon on Hawaiian guitar (courtesy of Phil Zimmerman)

MAUI CHIMES ♯ 1

54

MAUI CHIMES ♯2

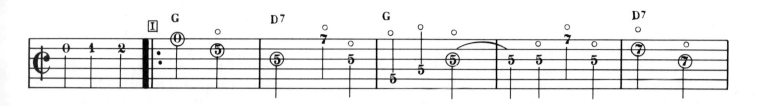

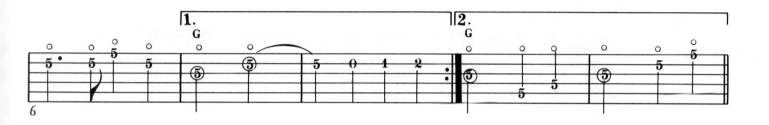

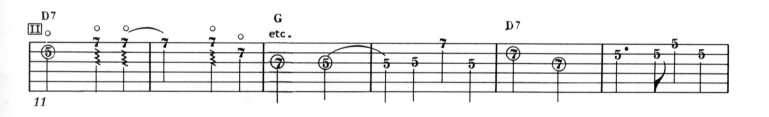

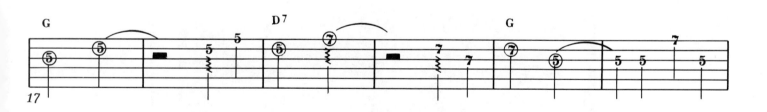

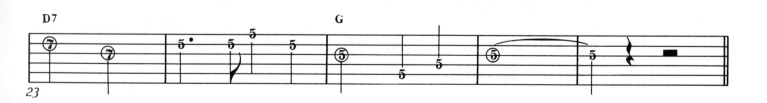

Where is the stomp in **"Honolulu Stomp"**? This is not a hula, but its approach is very first-generation steel guitar. It is credited to A. Cibella and the Hawaiian Serenaders on *Hula Blues* (Rounder 1012). How about a classification of "unrefined, Hawaiian ragtime march"? It is a relic of a simpler time, probably recorded in Patterson, New Jersey, or some such tropical clime.

This is one of the many tunes in this book originally recorded in the key of F in A tuning, which transposes to E♭ in G tuning. If you wish to play in F, tune the open strings to an A chord or buy a capo and put it on the 2nd fret. (An acoustic steel-guitar capo is available from me at 36 Cromwell Hill Road, Monroe, NY 10950.)

"Honolulu Stomp" is a goofy number. The pompous interludes have wacky chords, while the melody and phrasing might best be described as cornball. Still, all steel guitarists should be familiar with silly melodies. To warm up for this tablature, make a few funny noises on your guitar. Few instruments can match a steel's ability to come up with strange sounds.

Actually, I like this tune. Play at about MM = 116 in 2/4 meter. Good luck.

Stacy Phillips Trio (Bob Brozman and Bela Fleck on rhythm guitars)

HONOLULU STOMP

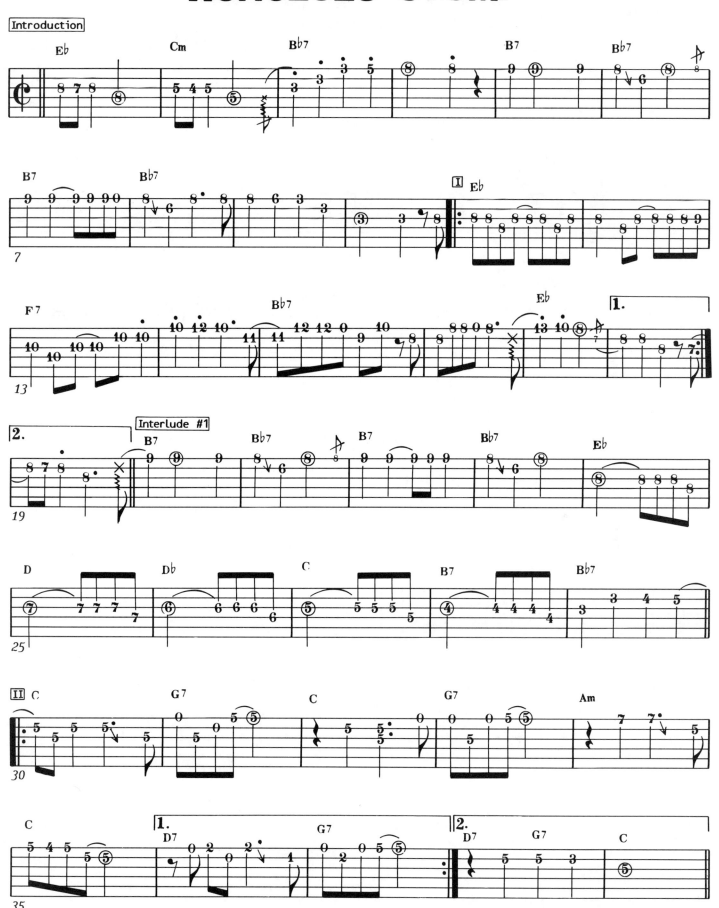

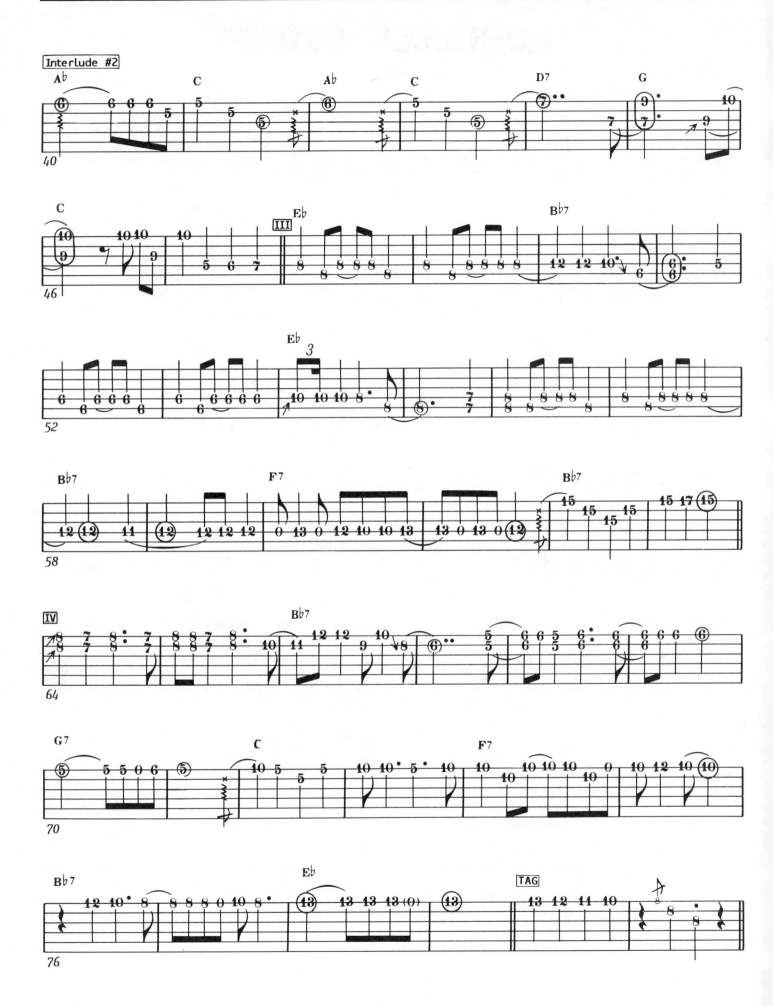

Kika Kila — Mai Ka "A" A Ka "W"
"Steel Guitar — from 'A' to 'W'"

Now for some full-tilt Hawaiian-steel classics calling on the full range of technique or, as the chapter title would have it, the entire Hawaiian alphabet (which only goes to the letter "w.")

There are more variations of the melodies in this portion of the book, including some hot "take-off" solos in the style that entered the Hawaiian musical lexicon in the late 1920s. There is much less staccato phrasing and hiccupping with open strings.

Some demanding and tricky bar maneuvers are ahead, so gird your loins and steel your nerves.

"Mai Kai No Kauai" honors Kauai Island's scenery and its chief Kaumuahi. The following arrangement is based on the playing of Tau Moe. Play this at a cut-time tempo of *MM* = 136. That is *MM* = 68 when played in 2/4 meter.

Each of the final eighth notes in the first three measures is really a hiccup-type note and should be held somewhere between an eighth and a sixteenth note. Remember to try to imitate the sound of a voice breaking from standard tone to falsetto.

Measure 6 illustrates another steel-guitar move that has its antecedents in the vocals of ancient *meles* — sliding to a tone (here a 13/12 double stop) just in advance of that same tone being picked. A variation of measures 7 and 8 follows the main melody. The opening string 3, fret 9, replaces the last eighth-note duration of

the string 1, fret 13/string 3, fret 12, double stop of measure 6.

A version of this tune can be heard on *Vintage Hawaiian Music — The Great Singers* (Rounder 1053).

Tau Moe (courtesy of Bob Brozman)

MAI KAI NO KAUAI

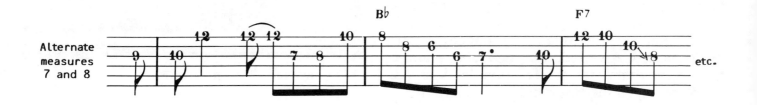

"Lei Ana Ika Mokihana" refers to a garland of the fruit of the *mokihana* tree. What a mellifluous title! The first verse is based on Mike Hanapi's playing *(Early Hawaiian Classics,* Folklyric 9022) and the second is a mix of Hanapi and Bob Brozman *(Hello Central . . . Give Me Dr. Jazz,* Rounder 3086).

The last four measures of the first verse give hints of a certain amount of blues sensibility in Mr. Hanapi. String 1, fret 6, is the flatted third (blues) third of an F chord. Check out Hanapi's beautiful phrasing in measures 15–16. And, of course, there are neatly turned turnarounds in measures 9–10 and 17–20.

There is no note overlapping in this rendition, so play everything but the last measure with the tip of the bar. The tempo is around MM = 116.

LEI ANA IKA MOKIHANA

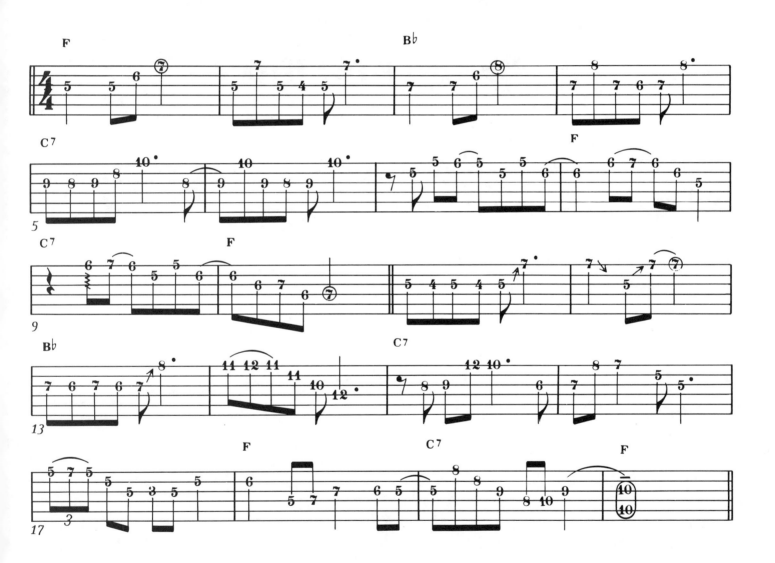

Dick McIntire was a very popular player in the 1930s and '40s, appearing mostly in Hawaii. He was an early master of the electric steel. I am not sure of the tuning he used on *"Ke Ahi Kuu Ipo,"* but it works well in standard G major. The one sacrifice to the tuning is in measure 8, which McIntire plays:

The way I have tabbed it bars a bit easier and sounds at least as cool.

His handling of the turnaround licks, beginning at measure 7, is especially noteworthy — melodically more complex than previous ones in this book, but smooth and elegant. Play this at about MM = 128 with decidedly swing eighths.

KE AHI KUU IPO

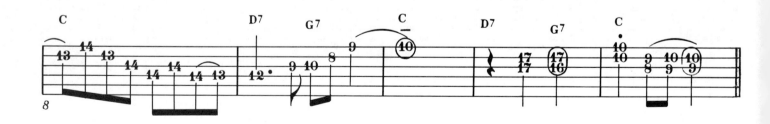

"Na Pua O Hawaii" is basically a series of charming turnarounds. It's one after the other, 'round and 'round in a dizzying series of turns. Charles Opununi (whose version on *Vintage Hawaiian Music — Steel Guitar Masters,* Rounder 1052, is the basis of this tablature) squeezes out some of my favorite tricone tone.

Depending on your steel orientation, a National tricone sounds like 1) an exquisite series of bells, or 2) a very expensive rubber band. (There has been a long, raucous, whine-filled history of petty warfare involving partisans of wood-bodied resonator guitars vs. single-resonator metal bodies vs. tricone metal bodies vs. six-string electric lap steels vs. eight-string lap steels vs. aluminum-bodied steels vs. bakelite-bodied steels vs. 99% of the rest of the guitar-playing population who probably have not heard of Hawaiian guitar.)

The second verse modulates from the key of C of G♭. The final stanza is similar, but with an extra turnaround tacked on. Play at a cut-time tempo of about MM = 132.

Les Adams and group in Australia (courtesy of Dirk Vogel)

NA PUA O HAWAII

"*Ua Like No A Like*" is an intense love song composed by Alice Everett in the 1880s. The title is freely translated as "sweet constancy" or "my heart's choice." This arrangement is based on the vocal harmonies of the Moe Family on their recent album (Rounder 6028). The story of their decades-long world tour is the stuff of show-business legend. Hopefully some of their adventures and music will become better known if a projected documentary film about them comes to fruition.

Play very slowly, with much vibrato and legato phrasing. Experiment with some tremolo and artificial harmonies. Drag out the slides.

This tune is a good candidate for the anticipated slide phrasing mentioned in the introduction to "*Mai Kai No Kauai.*" For example, measure 12 could be authentically phrased:

Likewise, measure 17 could be:

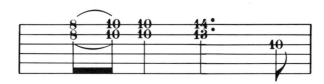

Watch for the dangerous series of double stops in measures 25–26. Straight bar to forward slant to straight to reverse, sliding to a forward slant is a pretty nasty assignment. Until you drop your bar a few times during your struggle to master such tortuous maneuvers, you cannot be considered a full-fledged member of the society of steelers.

UA LIKE NO A LIKE

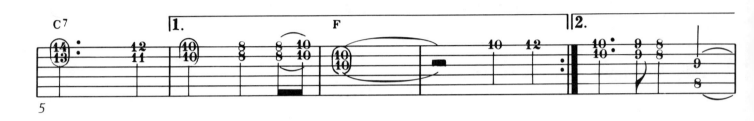

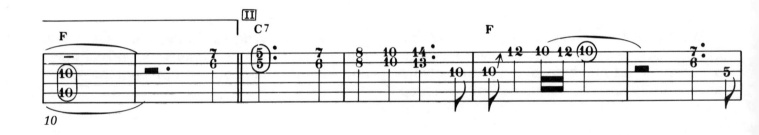

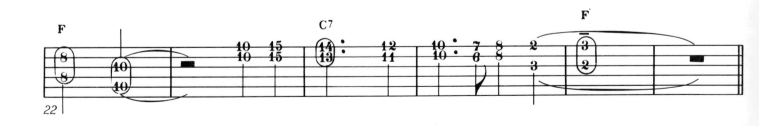

"*Lei Lehua*" is a bouncy *hapa haole*-type tune played at a cut-time tempo of about MM = 160. There is some quick single-string work, especially in the jazzy second verse. Play the latter with decided swing eighths.

As with most tremolo interludes, do not damp the strings between frets, and vibrato for all you're worth — fast enough for the individual pitches of the notes to become blurred and a gurgling, sobbing effect to emerge.

Measure 19 is tricky to read. Do not block for the first three beats, alternately picking strings 1 and 3 and letting them ring. Block the strings before the last 12/10 double-stop slide to 13/11, and pick the latter on the downbeat of measure 20. Well done!

Sol Hoopii virtually invented this category of Hawaiian swing. His recording of this tune was played in the same key but on a guitar tuned to A, allowing him a couple of open-string licks not possible in this arrangement. (For example, the grace note in measure 11 would be an open first string in A tuning.) His version can be heard on *Sol Hoopii — Volume One* (Rounder 1024).

The *lehua* is a staple of many Hawaiian proverbs, where it signifies beauty and expertise.

LEI LEHUA

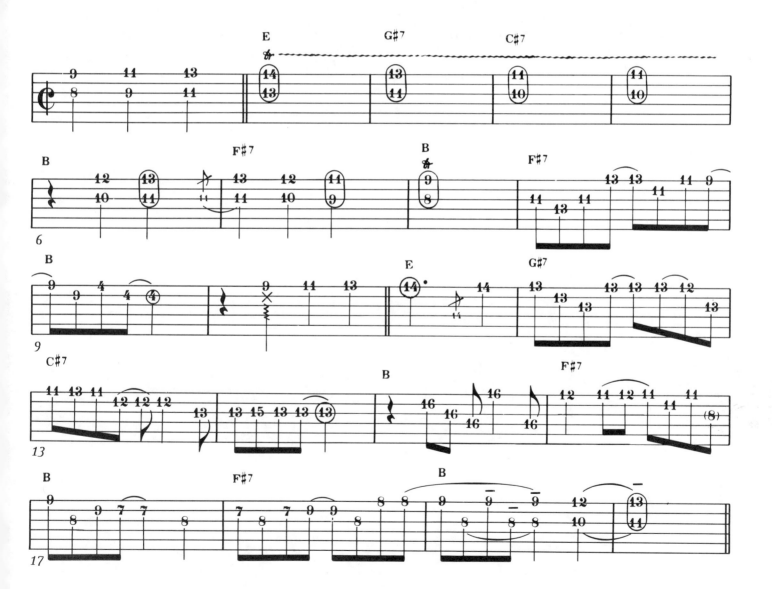

"Kiho' Alu" is liberally adapted from the slack-key playing of Gabby Pahinui. Slack-key is probably the earliest "Hawaiianized" guitar style, emerging from the idea of tuning the strings of a standard guitar down to an open chord. Pahinui was a pivotal figure in the renaissance of traditional Hawaiian music in the 1970s.

This is another tune with a straightforward melody made interesting (and, coincidentally, difficult to sight read) by syncopated phrasing. This arrangement is peppered with double stops that are picked separately, then allowed to overlap; e.g., measures 2, 4, 5, 12, 14, 15, 21, etc.

Many of the rhythmic figures are typical of slack-key phrasing; e.g., measures 1, 7, 21, and 35. The second strain is the first one raised an octave.

Measure 34 has another chant-based anticipated slide. (See *"Mai Kai No Kauai."*) Measure 35 is a cool lick that works best out of slant positions even though there is no note overlap. Check out the way Pahinui has taken what is basically a bit of a scale,

```
--17--------15----------------
--16--------14----------------
------------------------------
------------------------------
------------------------------
------------------------------
```

broken it into pieces, added a little tinsel and syncopation, and created an exciting riff.

Play this at a 2/4 tempo of MM = 78, and slow down during the last two measures. The term *"kiho' alu"* refers to slack-key guitar.

KIHO' ALU

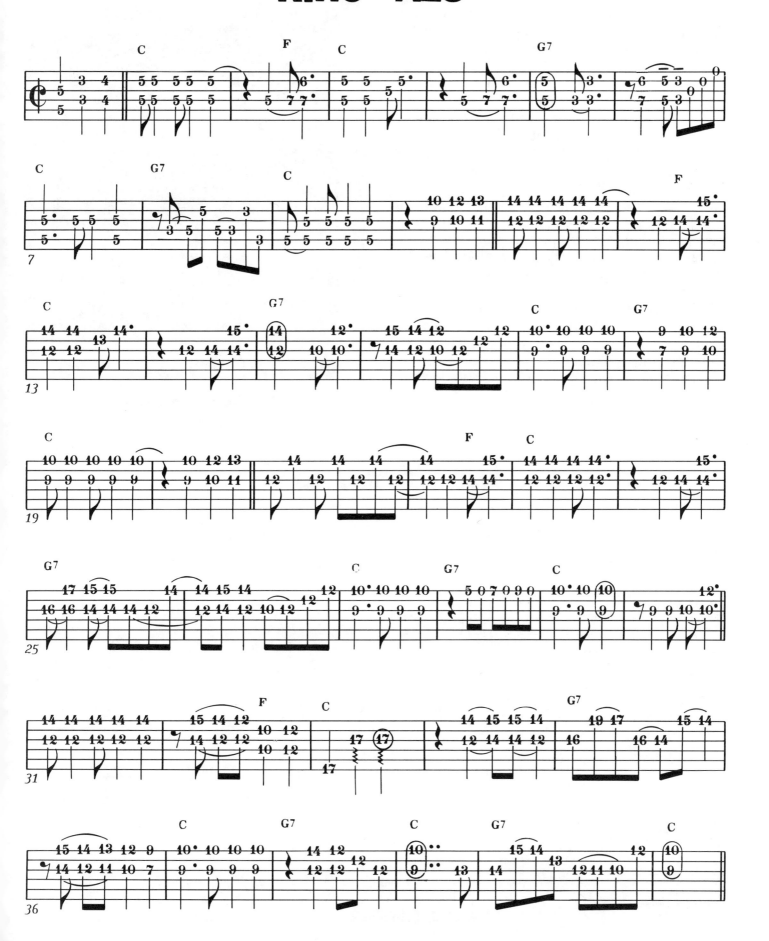

"Na Moku Eha" is based on the scintillating stylings of Bob Brozman, a current expert on old Hawaiian guitar. It is the second tune in his **"Hawaiian Heat Waves Medley"** on *Hello Central* (Rounder 3086). In cut time, play this at MM = 140, which comes out frisky but not fast.

The half-note triplets of measures 7 and 9 are tricky to time. Try counting these measures in straight 2/4 meter. This will make each triplet last only one quarter note — much easier to count.

The second verse commences with four measures of all-out boogie tremolos. The whole piece is unmistakably full-tilt Hawaiian. The title may refer to the pain of separation.

Mr. Brozman is currently at work on a book about the National Guitar Company, its history and instruments. It will be published by Centerstream, a subsidiary of Hal Leonard Publishing. All instrument fetishists should keep an eye out for it.

Bob Brozman (courtesy of Bob Brozman)

NA MOKU EHA

Charles Opununi's version of *"Na Ali'i"* begins with a fast triplet double stop. At a cut-time tempo of MM = 160, it would probably be easiest to play this figure using your thumb and index finger like a flat pick. Pick both strings of the first double stop with the thumb, the second double stop picking down with the index or middle finger, and the third with the thumb again. Then your index and middle fingers are ready for the 10th-fret double stop that begins the first measure.

Opununi's staccato is not nearly as pronounced as those in some of the old hulas we have met. Leave only a very small pause be-tween the notes. His vibrato, like Sol Hoopii's, is timed in triplets and about ½ fret above and below the indicated frets.

The heat is turned up a few notches in the variation of the verse. The third-string maneuver in measure 17 is difficult to play smoothly. Do not cheat on the duration of the notes on frets 10 and 9 in haste to reach fret 7 on time. You could play fret 7 as an open first string, but I detect a vibrato in Opununi's playing.

Measures 21–23 are another riff that is difficult to decide on an unambiguous barring. It could be played:

"Na ali'i" means "the chiefs," and the lyrics, composed by Samuel Kuahiwi, urge the listener to remember the wisdom of departed ancestors.

"Ua pau, ua hala lakou,
A koe no na pua."

"They are gone, they have passed,
And their flowers survive."

A recording of this song can be found on *Vintage Hawaiian Music — Steel Guitar Masters* (Rounder 1052).

NA ALI'I

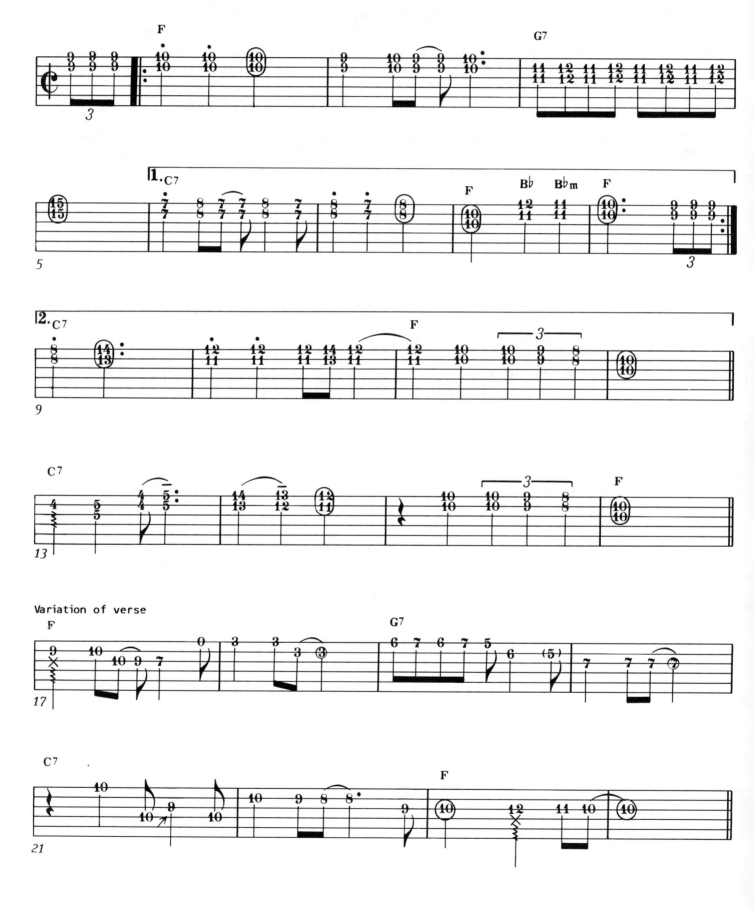

"Na Lei O Hawaii" (usually called **"Song of the Islands,"** though more literally "Flowers of the Islands") was written by Charles E. King. He continued the *hula kui* style of composition. He wanted Hawaiian tunes to be played slowly and not jazzed up. The first verse of this arrangement follows his precepts; but the second, starting at measure 21, blatantly indulges in the kind of treatment King frequently railed against. It is courtesy of Hal Aloma, who, I am sure, has nothing personal against Mr. King.

Note the displacement of the measure-4 lick in measure 24. Then there is the devilish reverse slant and pull in measure 26. In this position, the 2-fret pull is not as difficult as you might think. (It is harder to conceive this bar position that it is to play it.) This formation makes a D13 chord. I take responsibility for it.

Measures 29–35 are a nicely constructed swing solo, but firmly rooted in *hapa haole* style. The last eight measures are a double turn-around. Check out the chord progression.

"Na Lei O Hawaii" is one of the most popular Hawaiian tunes of all time. The original lyrics deal with the typical flowers of each major island.

"Hanohano Hawai'i,
Elei ha'aheo nei i ka lehua."

"Majestic Hawaii,
adorned with garlands of *lehua."*

NA LEI O HAWAII

by C. E. King (1915)

Retunings

In the search for easy ways to play the jazzy, embellished chords of the pop music of their day, Hawaiian guitarists investigated tunings that were not straight major chords. Every time American swing musicians came up with a new progression, voicing, or harmonic extension, steelers explored new ways of setting up their strings to put the new sounds in reach of one straight metal bar.

I have tabbed examples in some of the most enduring and influential versions in the context of solos by a few of the greatest players. Many of the tunings were invented during the development of the sweet, legato approach to this music. This is reflected in this chapter by the absence, except for **"Indiana March,"** of staccato phrasing.

Ladies and gentlemen, drain your tension and start your vibratos.

The key of D (sometimes E) is the other original major-chord steel-guitar tuning derived from slack-key style — from high to low strings, D-A-F♯-D-A-D. *He Aloha Noa Honolulu"* is a good candidate to illustrate the relationship between G and D tunings. This is the kind of situation where some familiarity with the jargon of music theory can be illuminating. I can see your eyes glazing over already. Please, a bit of patience — don't worry, be happy.

A comparison of the first two measures of this melody in each tuning reveals most of the story. Note that what is played on the top two strings in G is played 5 frets higher on strings 2 and 3 in D tuning. The theoretical basis for this can be stated quite simply (heh! heh!). The top two strings of G tuning (D and B) are the fifth and third steps, respectively, of a G scale; while the second and third strings of D tuning (A and F♯)

are also the fifth and third steps, but of the key of D. Since the intervals between these two sets of strings are the same, the same bar positions can be used.

Finally, since both the A and F♯ notes of the D tuning are 5 frets lower than the equivalent D and B of G tuning, there is a 5-fret difference in bar placement. Eureka!

Also note the difference in fretting when playing double stops on the first- and third-string double stops. Because of the 1-fret difference in the third strings in these tunings, there is a 1-fret difference in slant position. Thus, G tuning's 2-fret slants become 1-fret slants in D; and 1-fret slants become straight positions. If a tune calls for many first- and third-string combinations, it would be marginally easier to play in D tuning.

These tuning transformations are explained for two reasons: 1) to help you search for bar positions when you work up new tunes, and 2) to help you transpose a melody to another tuning.

The lyrics of this tune concern a 19th-century boat trip from Honolulu to Maui to Hawaii Island. Play at a sprightly cut-time tempo of MM = 130–148, with decidedly swingy eighth notes.

The tune begins and ends with two turnarounds. There is a neat bar rotation at the end of measure 19 — contrary motion on the first and third strings, while the note on the second string stays the same.

Versions of *"He Aloha Noa Honolulu"* can be heard on *The Tau Moe Family with Bob Brozman* (Rounder 6028) and *Original Hawaiian Steel Guitar* with Tony Ku (Folkways 8714).

HE ALOHA NOA HONOLULU ♯ 1

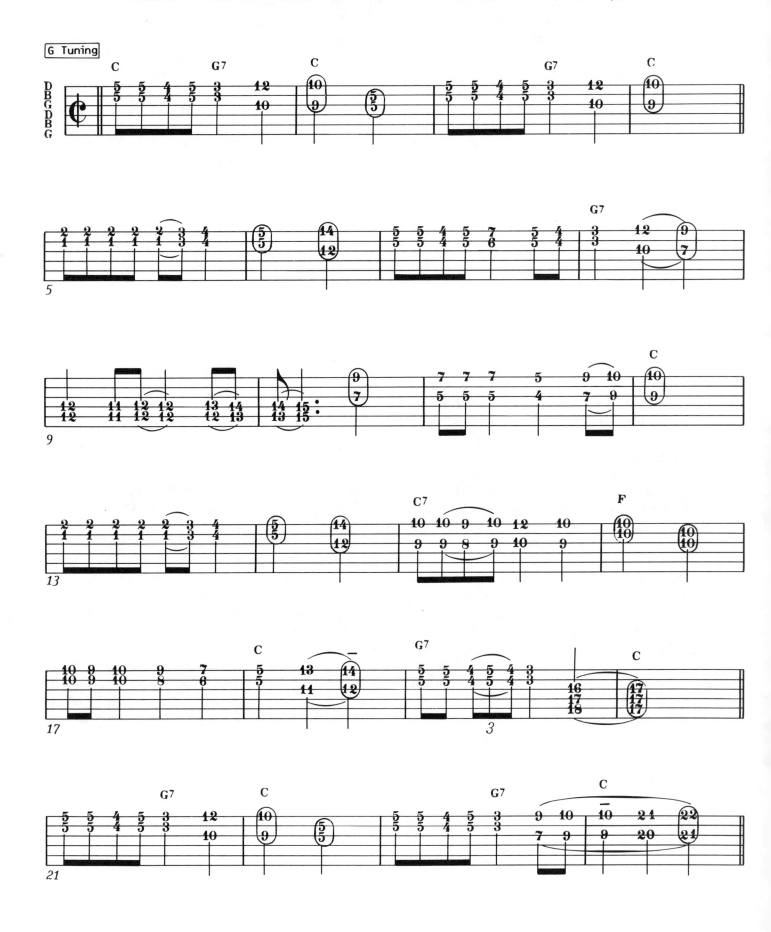

HE ALOHA NOA HONOLULU ♯2

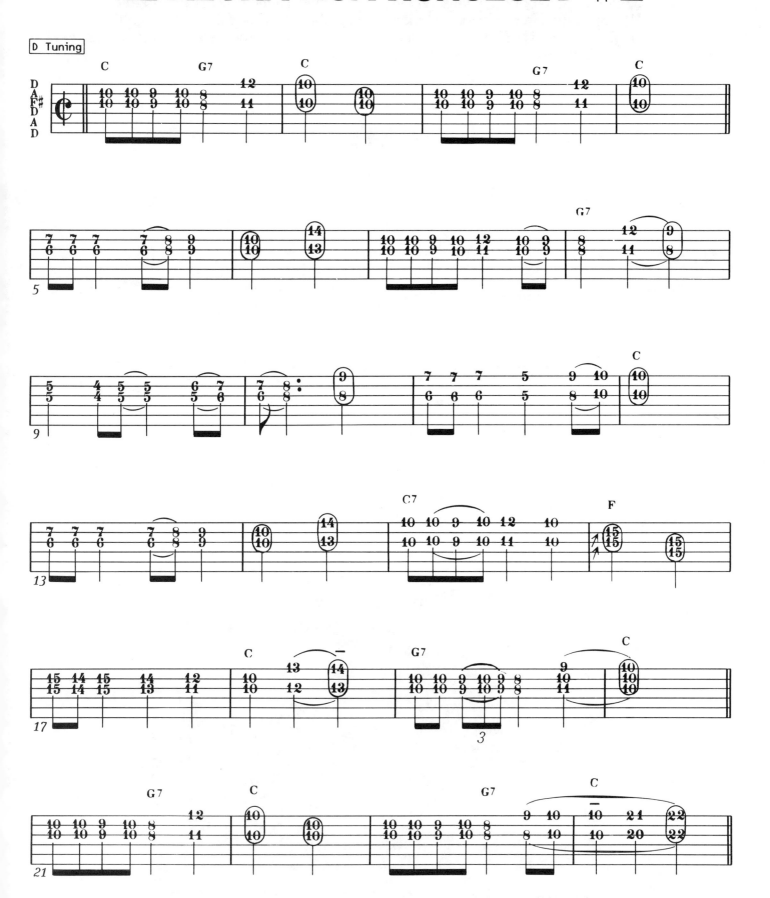

Dick McIntire took up the banner of steel when Sol Hoopii stopped touring extensively in the 1930s. McIntire pioneered experimentation with new tunings, such as F#9 (from high to low strings: E-C#-G#-E-A#-F#). He was extremely influential in establishing the now-predominant *nahenahe* legato style.

"Hilo E" is adapted from his arrangement in E tuning (our D). This is another tune pieced together with Hawaiian vamps, with the actual turnaround in the last two measures. Play at about MM = 126.

HILO E

Dick McIntire and His Harmony Hawaiians: *Danny Kuaana (ukulele), Al McIntire (bass), Dick McIntire (steel), Lani McIntire (guitar) (courtesy of Dirk Vogel)*

"Paahana #2" is based on the Dick McIntire version of the song. (The first version is in the *"Ho'i Ana I Ke Kumu"* chapter.) The key is the same, but examine the effect of the different tuning. A new section pops up in measure 16. Play at about MM = 132.

PAAHANA #2

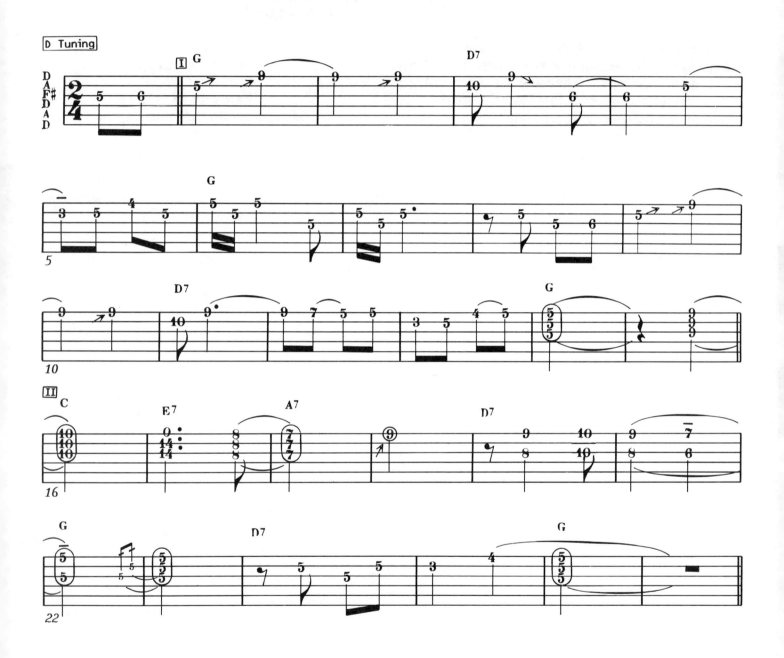

"Aloha Oe" ("Farewell to Thee") is the song most identified with Hawaii. It was composed by the last monarch of the Islands, Queen Lydia Lili'uokalani. Although it is now often used as a song of farewell, it was originally conceived as a love ballad. It is possible that the queen wrote this in prison shortly after the planters' coup of 1887, as good a reason as any for its melancholy sweetness.

The melody of "Aloha Oe" makes D tuning a good choice because of all the first- and third-string double stops. In measure 4, hold the 14/13 double stop until the last eighth note of its duration, and then quickly slide to fret 10.

In measure 18 you can use a tricky tactic to avoid jumping all the way down to the 5th fret for the artificial harmonics: Move to a straight bar on fret 10, and play the harmonics with your right hand on fret 17. Pick the same strings that the tablature shows as the 5th fret. Notice that, whether you bar fret 5 or 10, your picking hand still touches fret 17. This alternative pitches the notes an octave higher.

"Aloha 'oe,
E ke onaona i ka lipo."

"Farewell to you,
O fragrance in the blue depths."

ALOHA OE

Repeat
section I
with second
ending

Apparently, Sol Hoopii was the first to use Bm tuning, dropping the third string (and sometimes the sixth) by 1 fret. The relation between Bm and D tunings makes the former seem like a partial D tuning. This kinship is made more obvious by its Bm7 variation (see **"Hoopii Hot Solo"** and **"Hula Blues #3"**). The only difference between the latter and D is the pitch of the second string. From Hoopii's A tuning (top three strings: E-C♯-A), slacking the third string makes a C♯ minor (E-C♯-G♯).

For those of you with some background in music theory, D-B-F♯ also makes up three of the notes of Gma7, E9, and D6 chords, all with a straight bar on fret 12 or open.

"Indiana March" is based on Hoopii's version, in which he uses the third string sparingly. At MM = 130, this piece is a formidable exercise. As usual, take it as slowly as necessary until you can play in a steady, deliberate tempo.

The third string is finally plucked in section II, where the forward roll in measures 24–25 makes a G6 chord (in the position that would sound a C chord in standard G tuning). To duplicate this in standard G, you have to play:

The first- and third-string double stops in measures 26, 27, 41, and 49 would have been 1-fret slants without retuning.

Section III modulates to C and features a finger-popping riff in measures 43 and 45. Notice that the second string has a tie, while the first is picked.

Section IV, beginning at measure 52, is a fanfare-like presentation with lots of octaves. You have to keep your thumb and index (or middle) finger pinching at a pretty good rate to fit in all the notes. At the end of section IV, repeat sections III, IV, then III again, ending at "coda."

Recordings of **"Indiana March"** can be heard on *Sol Hoopii — Volume 2* (Rounder 1025) and *Hula Blues* (Rounder 1012). On the latter, it is called **"Hawaiian March."** This version of the tune is from the latter period of Sol Hoopii's recording career. In 1938 he became an adherent of the evangelical superstar Aimee Semple McPherson and rejected playing pop and jazz. Apparently, marches are less secular.

As far as I can tell, there is no place called Indiana on the Islands.

Sol Hoopii (courtesy of Tony Todaro)

INDIANA MARCH

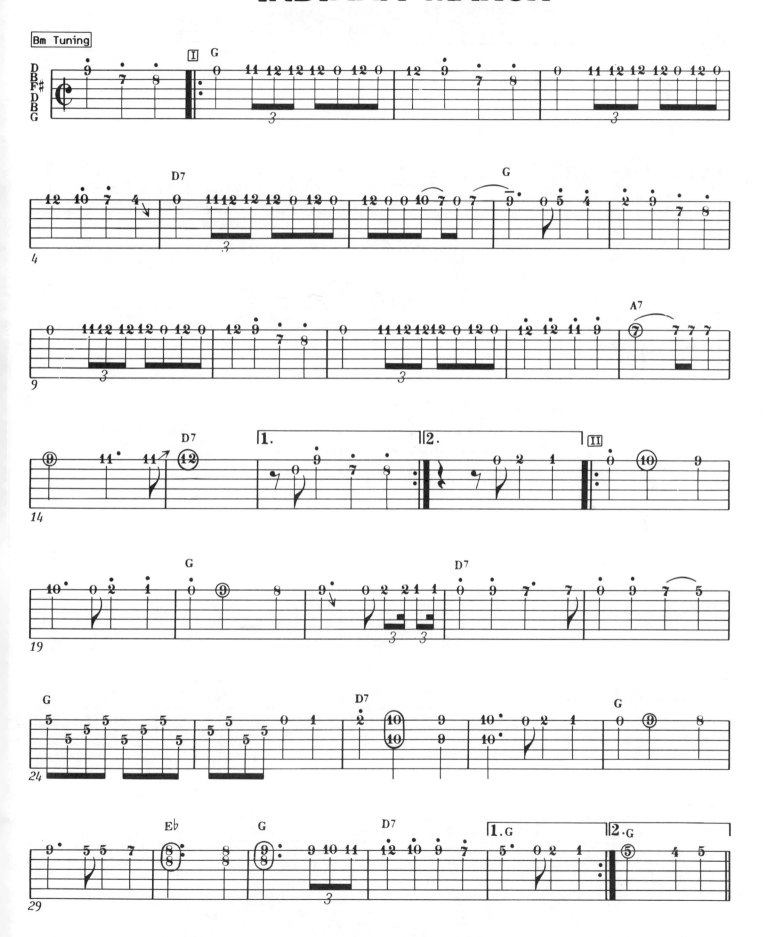

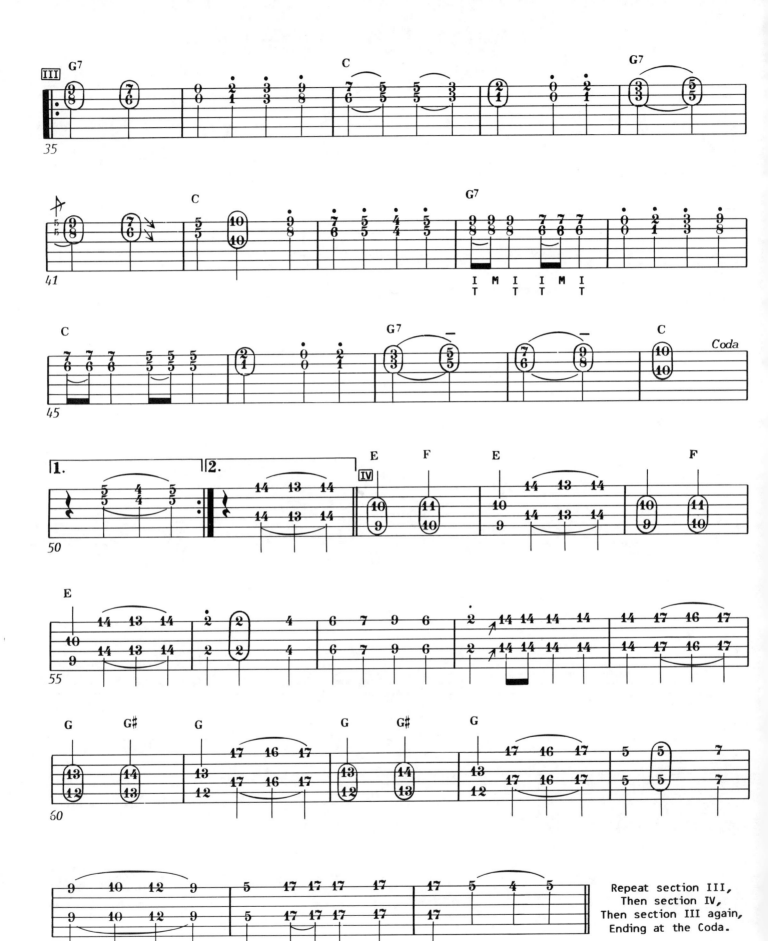

Repeat section III,
Then section IV,
Then section III again,
Ending at the Coda.

Hawaii was not the only exotic culture to mesmerize the West in the early 20th century. The Argentine gaucho and the tango of Buenos Aires were also alien and non-threatening. It was a natural for the two styles to be clumped together, as in **"La Rosita."** Section II is always played to a tango beat, while section I occasionally swings.

This tablature contains elements of versions by Bob Nichols (with the Lani McIntire Band), Sol K. Bright, Bob Brozman, and myself. Recordings can be heard on *Hawaiian Steel Guitar Classics, Volume 2* (Folklyric 9027) and *Hello Central… Give Me Dr. Jazz* (Rounder 3086). Play between MM = 100–120.

This arrangement features barrages of three-string chords in an embryonic swing approach. To break up the long series of three-finger pinches, you can play some of the chords as quick forward rolls:

The first- and second-string stuff in sections II and III are identical to what would be played in G tuning.

Play very legato up to the variation of section I beginning at measure 48. The next two sections are played on the staccato side. At the end of measure 49, start the slide immediately. Land on fret 15 on the next downbeat. The same is true of the long slide in measure 58, landing on fret 20 on the downbeat.

The slides in measure 50 are short, fast, and damped at the end, resulting in a harmonized, chirping sound. In measure 56, they are slower, slier, and not damped. Their speed increases in measure 57. The composite effect is one of increasing agitation as the last three sections roll by.

There is a twist to the tremolos of measures 64–69. Alternate picking the thumb on the third string and a middle/index-finger double stop as quickly as possible. Do not damp during the tremolo. Slide in a dangerously loose fashion (a la M. K. Moke) while vibratoing like a broken-down washing machine. What a pixilated tune!

George Kainapau (ukulele), Al McIntire (bass), Bob Nichols (National tricone), Lani McIntire (guitar) (courtesy of Dirk Vogel)

LA ROSITA

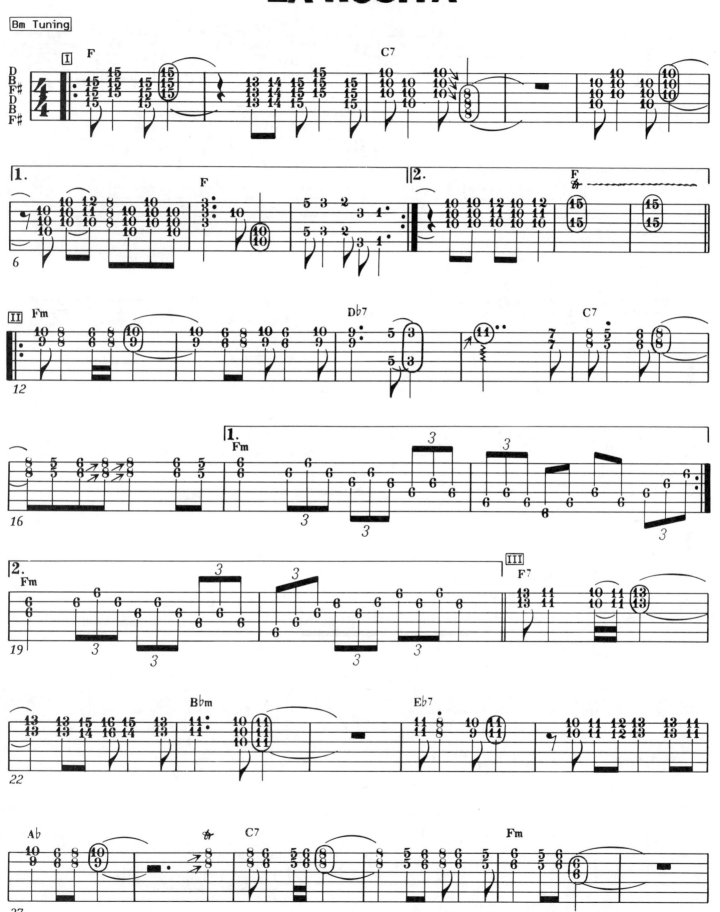

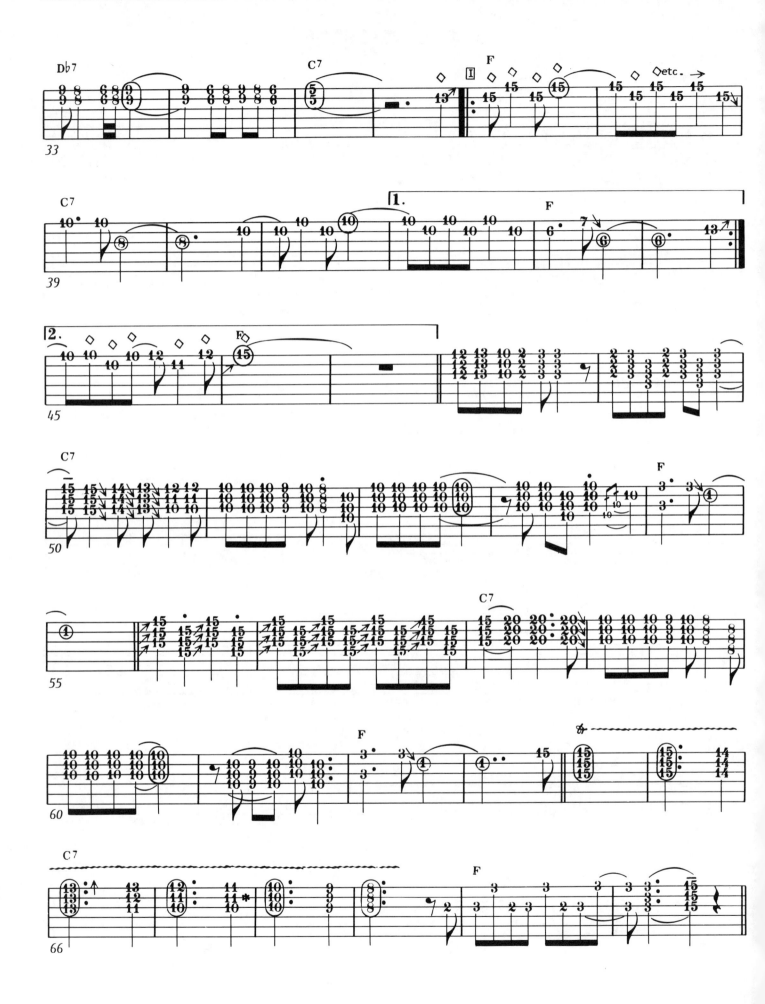

The next tablature shows the kind of chords that Sol Hoopii had in mind when he formulated Bm tuning. This solo is taken from one of his improvisations from 1920s pop music (for example, **"Fascinating Rhythm"**). His bar phrasing is not Hawaiian-style legato, but typical swing.

Note that Hoopii makes one change to the Bm tuning, lowering the pitch of the fifth string from B to A, thus making the open chord a Bm7.

Hoopii begins with a blast resembling a bleary-eyed trumpet section with an opening C9 chord. The first two measures illustrate the three typical chord positions of Bm(7) tuning:

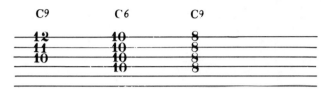

The slides in measure 5, 13, and 23 are faster than the other glissandos in this piece. The weirdest-sounding chord is the C9 augmented that surfaces like an unwelcome guest in measures 15–16:

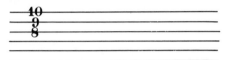

It helps to have an open mind and ear when faced with such new sounds. Actually, if you play with absolute conviction, almost anything can be foisted upon the listening public.

It sounds as if the 19/18/18 triplet stop in measure 23 is played as a fudge slant, but you might try it as a straight position with a pulled first string:

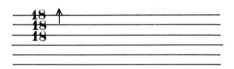

In the last two measures, there is a gapped chord that takes advantage of the A string. Now you can play a full F-major triad on fret 15 (or 3) using strings 1, 3, 4, 5, and 6 (what used to be a Bb position in G tuning).

Play at medium jitterbug tempo, cut-time meter of MM = 190.

SOL HOOPII HOT SOLO

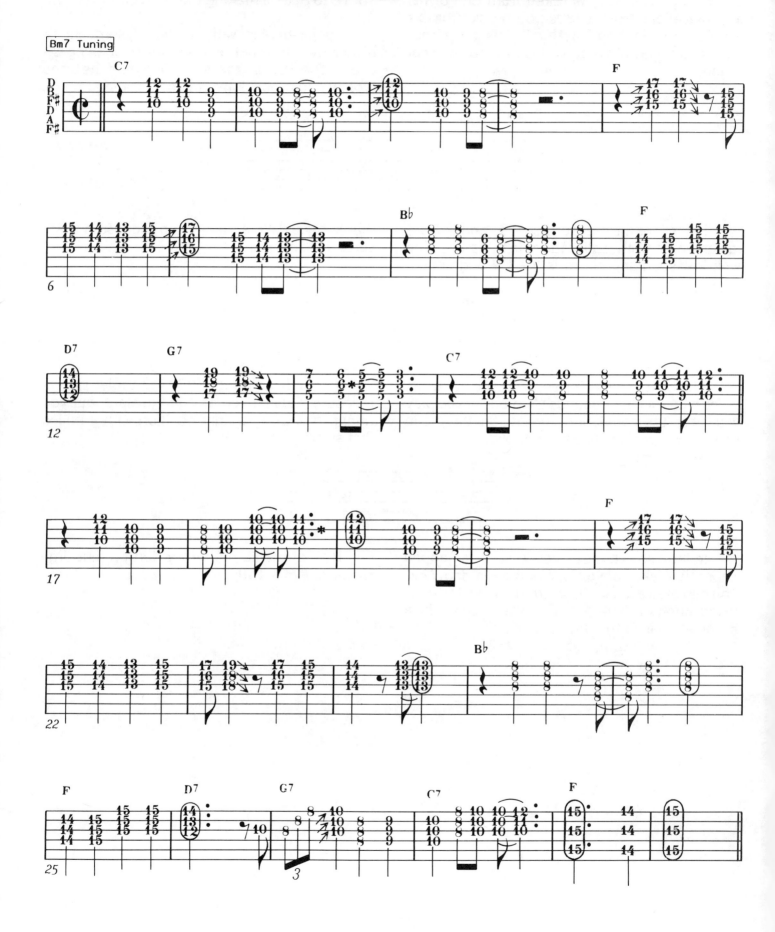

C6 is a relatively late development in novel steel tunings. To avoid changing strings (C is pitched 5 frets higher than G, so thinner-gauged strings would be required), your guitar can be slack-tuned to G6. (The slacked strings will be a bit loose to sound their best, but the alternatives are either changing strings or buying another guitar.) If you already use C6 tuning, play the tablatures as written, and all the chords will sound 5 frets higher — so C transposes to F; Bb to Eb; etc.

I chose the *hapa haole* ditty **"Little Heaven of the South Seas"** to illustrate some relationships between G and G6. The first arrangement is in standard G. Play it at a dreamy MM = 84. There is an interesting modulation in section II.

To get to G6 tuning, lower the first string to match the second (B), and then the second string down to match the third (G). Now what was played in G tuning on the second and third strings can be duplicated on the first and second strings of G6. (Compare the fret-13 double stop that begins section II in both tunings.) The third string is lowered to an E note, 2 frets higher than the fourth string (D). E is the sixth step of a G scale, hence the name of the tuning. The bottom three strings stay the same. (In C6 the tuning would be, from high to low strings: E-C-A-G-E-C.)

The added sixth note makes minors and some embellished chords easier to play (similar to the Bm7 tuning), and the major second interval between the third and fourth strings is an added-bonus. It is now easier to play some single-note runs more smoothly, as will be shown in *"Alekoki"* and *"Kaua I Ka Huahua'i."*

Notice that the interval between G and E (strings 2 and 3) is 3 frets, the same as between D and B (strings 1 and 2 of G tuning). Therefore, to duplicate what you played on strings 1 and 2 in G, play the same bar positions in G6, but one string lower and 7 frets higher. The latter makes up for the 7-fret difference between a G note and a D note. There are examples of this in *"E Mama E."*

Here is one more comparison that deals directly with **"Little Heaven of the South Seas:"** The intervals between the first and third strings of both tunings are the same, but the notes are 3 frets lower in G6; so the 14/12-fret double stop in measure 1 in G tuning becomes the equivalent 17/15 in measure 6 in **"Little Heaven #2."**

G6 requires a dramatic reconception of where to look for notes. It is the basis for one of the current standard tunings of the pedal steel.

A "chimes" section introduces the proceedings in **"Little Heaven #2"** in G6. The prelude climaxes with an octave-long, languid slide.

"Little Heaven of the South Seas #3" is a more chordal approach. You can begin with the same artificial harmonics as in the previous version. Measure 1 features a nice reverse slant/pull that is worth struggling over. The voicing of the chords in this tuning seem mellower than those in the older Bm version.

A recording of **"Little Heaven of the South Seas"** can be heard on *Lone Star Rag* (CBS Encore 14390) played by Western swing ace Leon McAuliffe. He probably used an eight-string A6 tuning: from high to low strings, E-C#-A-F#-E-C#-A-F#.

LITTLE HEAVEN OF THE SOUTH SEAS ♯ 1

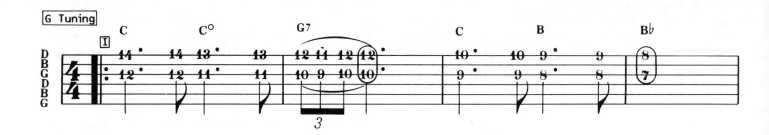

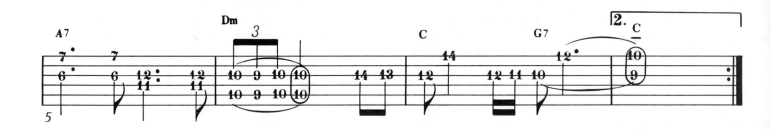

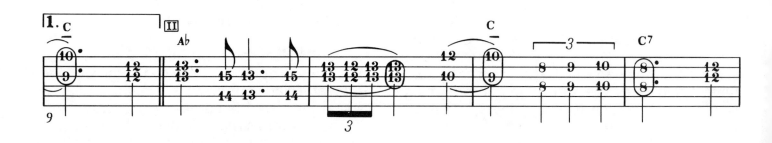

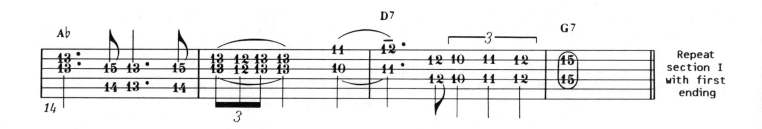

Repeat
section I
with first
ending

LITTLE HEAVEN OF THE SOUTH SEAS #2

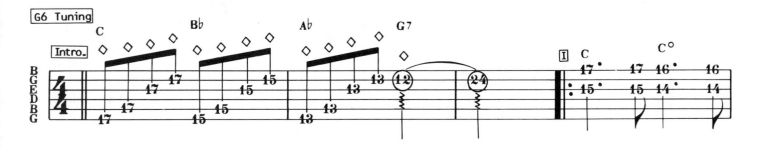

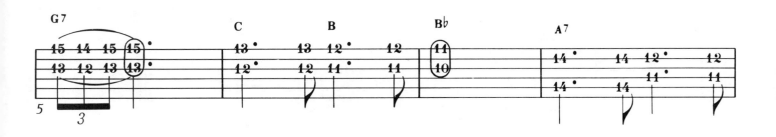

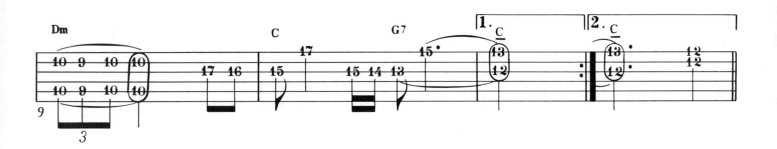

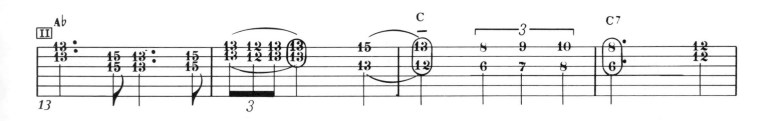

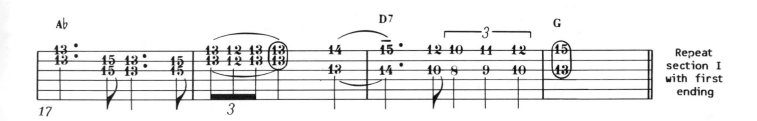

LITTLE HEAVEN OF THE SOUTH SEAS ♯3

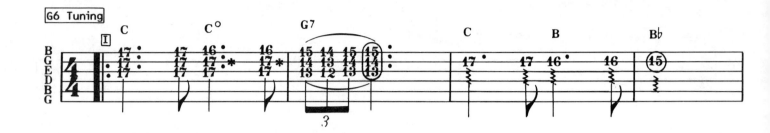

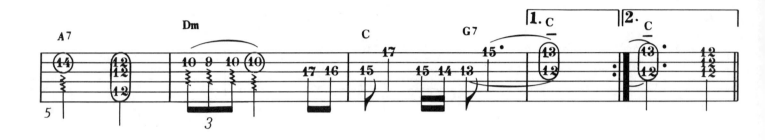

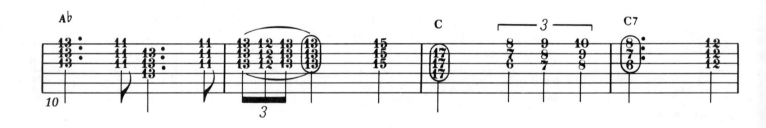

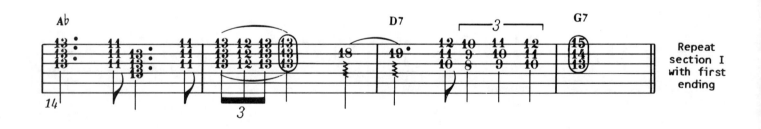

Repeat
section I
with first
ending

"Alekoki" is a classic piece based on an ancient chant. Several melodies have grown around the lyrics. The title refers to the Alekoki pool in Nu'uanu Stream near Kapena Falls in Honolulu. From Honolulu harbor the stream meanders to Jackass Ginger Pool and on through Nu'uanu Valley.

The first verse is a steel-guitar adaptation of the basic melody. Measure 6 has two typical chord positions for A7 (actually an A9 here). Play the fancy vamp in measures 7 and 9 with the tip of the bar. The "gapped" chord in the sixth measure is typical of this tuning. Usually either string 3 or 4 is omitted. Note that the same lick works over two different chord progressions in measures 7 and 9.

The second verse is based on the playing of David Kelii when he played with Al Kealoha Perry and his Singing Surfriders. It is quite jazzy but still has that typical Hawaiian feel. It illustrates some of the great single-string riffs now available with the addition of an E note to G tuning. Play at about MM = 116.

" *'A'ole i piliwi 'ia, Kahi wai a'o Alekoki.*"

"Unbelievable, waters of Alekoki."

David Kelii (courtesy of Tony Todaro)

ALEKOKI

Play *"E Mama E"* as legato as possible and as slowly as decay will allow, between MM = 60–70. In G tuning, the first two measures would be played:

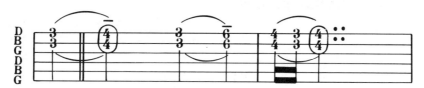

In measures 6–8, you should recognize that double stops on strings 2 and 4 in G tuning become double stops on strings 1 and 4 in G6. In measure 10, starting with string 4, fret 14, let the bar lie flat to allow overlap of the notes, including the slide to fret 16.

This tablature was inspired by the playing of Jerry Byrd, the most acclaimed Hawaiian-style player of his time. Byrd was a successful studio musician in Nashville, Tennessee, before moving to Hawaii in the early 1970s. The typical epithet applied to him is "master of touch and tone." He is a champion of smooth vibrato, clear harmonics, and diverse tunings. Byrd is a missionary of sorts for electric non-pedal steel and has sought to pass on his knowledge to a new generation through his teaching at music schools in Hawaii.

Byrd's version of *"E Mama E"* can be heard on *Byrd in Hawaii* (Maple 1002) and *Guitare Hawaienne Authentique* (Playasound 65027) played by John Kalapana.

E MAME E

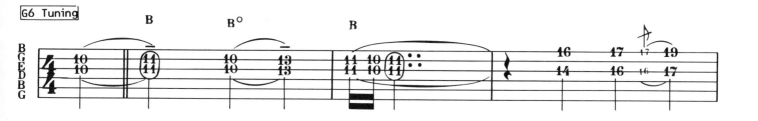

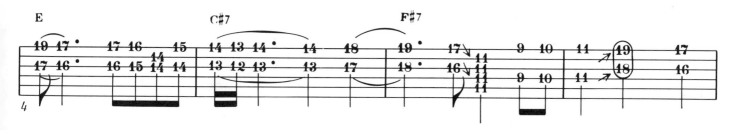

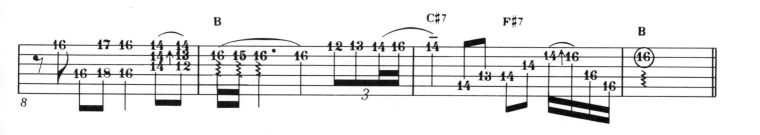

Lay that bar down, brothers and sisters. Here is an all natural-harmonics tune from Freddie Tavares by way of Jerry Byrd. (Is this the same Fred Tavares who had a hand in the evolution of the design of the pedal steel guitar?) G6 tuning opens up interesting melodic possibilities, even without a bar. Chord backup is really necessary to appreciate some of the nice twists in this tune. For example, string 5, fret 7, in measure 2 is the major seventh note of G; and string 3, fret 5, in measure 20 is the ninth note of the A7 chord.

You will need a velvet touch to get a clear, ringing harmonic from the lower strings, especially on the 5th fret. To improve your tone, you might try picking close to the bridge. Lift your fretting finger immediately after picking.

The really demanding lick comes in measure 27 with two high-velocity forward rolls. You cannot slide into a natural harmonic, so your left hand has to move very quickly to get both string 2, fret 12, and string 4, fret 7, notes sounding clearly. If this proves too strenuous, replace this measure with measure 19.

"Kewalo Chimes" can be heard on *Byrd in Hawaii* (Maple 1002). Kewalo Basin is a small inlet near downtown Honolulu. Play at about *MM* = 120.

KEWALO CHIMES

The melody of *"Kaua I Ka Huahua'i"* was written by Prince William Pitt Leleiohoku in the 1860s and later borrowed for the famous *hapa haole* tune **"The Hawaiian War Chant"** *("Ta-hu-wa-hu-wa-i")*. Leleiohoku was the younger brother of Queen Lili'uokalani. The title means "we two in the spray," a far cry from any war chants.

As usual, the first verse sticks closely to the basic melody (except measure 7), but with some syncopated rhythm — much crossing of the bar line and between the second and third beats of measures. Play with swing eighths.

The slides in section II are on all the strings you strum. In measure 12, do not strum string 6. You can reach for the second-string pull during the slide.

The second verse, beginning at measure 15, is a beautiful example of hot steel guitar. This style is usually associated with Western swing and country players, but obviously it is also a part of Hawaiian repertoire.

Part of this arrangement is based on the playing of Hal Aloma on *Musical Portrait of Hawaii* (Columbia C1 538). Play this at a 2/4 tempo of MM = 100.

*"Kaua i ka huahua'i,
E 'uhene la i pili ko'olua."*

"We two in the spray,
Oh joy, two together."

KAUA I KA HUAHUA' I ♯1

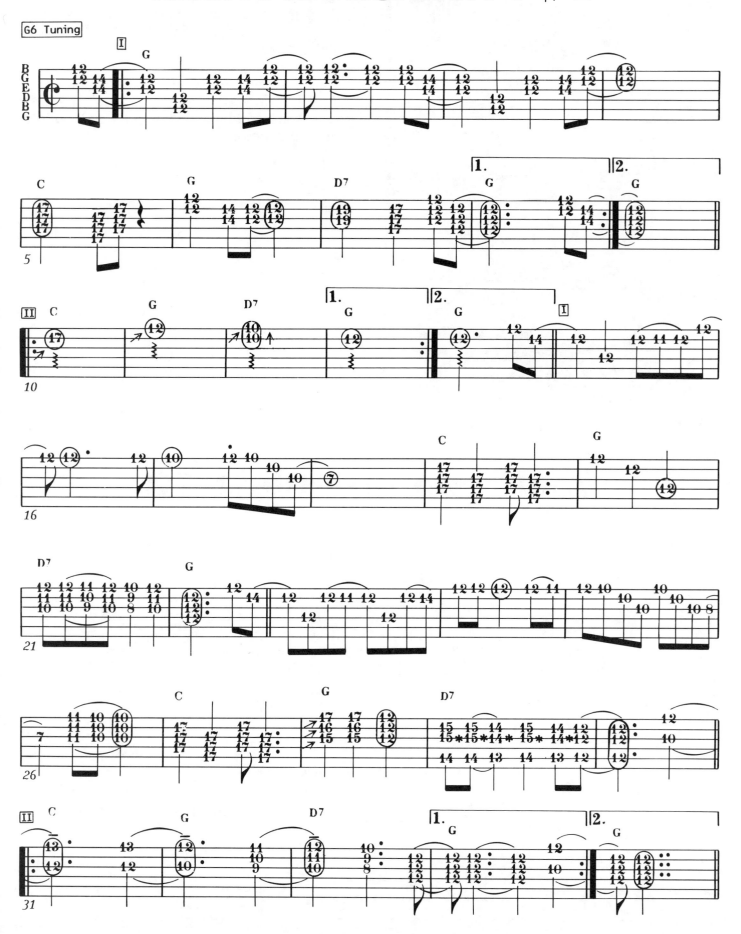

Andy Iona (courtesy of Tony Todaro)

Here is a version of the first section of *"Kaua I Ka Huahua'i"* in Bm tuning. It is from an arrangement by Andy (A)Iona's big *hapa haole* swing band. Iona was originally a fine Hawaiian-style saxophonist.

The second variation, beginning at measure 9, has only a few notes; but Iona's rhythmic prowess is formidable. He uses a deep, guttural tone at this point.

KAUA I KA HUAHUA' I #2

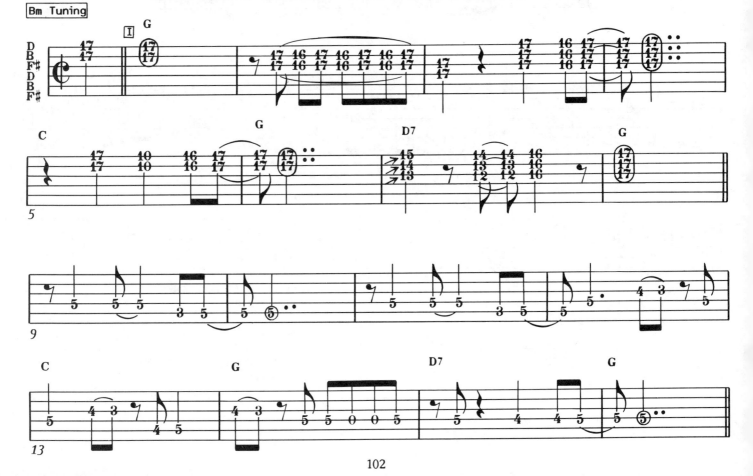

Hawaiian Guitar Extravaganzas

Here are some showcase show-off pieces. Each tune is a full meal that should inspire you to even greater flights of technical and artistic achievement. There is some high caloric content here, so digest this music slowly.

"Patches" is a *hapa haole* tune originally played in the key of C in A tuning by Sol Hoopii. Scuttlebutt has it that Mary Pickford, the silent-movie star, used to have Hoopii play to make her cry at appropriate moments on screen. Some of my own stylings have made music lovers weep uncontrollably.

Play this slowly enough to allow time to hit all the notes cleanly, and concentrate on a smooth, steady vibrato. The tempo should be about MM = 118. Recordings of this tune can be heard on *Sol Hoopii — Volume One* (Rounder 1024) and *The Emersons* (Mountain Apple 1008).

The triplet figure at the beginning of measure 15 is a literal notation of what Sol Hoopii played, but it should be considered an ornament. It might be more accurate to conceive it as being played:

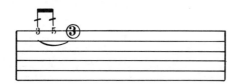

Measures 17–22 should be phrased as languidly as possible, even sluggishly. The timing here is not unlike the sound of a rubber ball falling down a flight of stairs in slow motion. Start the indicated slides immediately upon picking. Time them to reach fret 1 on the next beat, and immediately drop the bar down one string.

At the end of measures 25 and 27, you have to angle the bar back a bit into a slight reverse slant in order to get a continuous, seamless sound between the hiccupped note and the next measure.

The second verse, beginning at measure 33, is jazzier, with some tricky timing and quick bursts of bar movement. In measure 43 the slide almost makes it to fret 5.

PATCHES

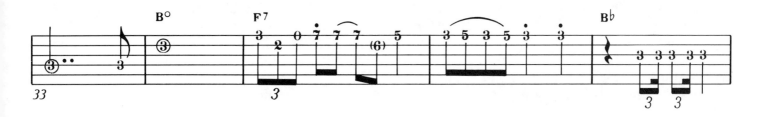
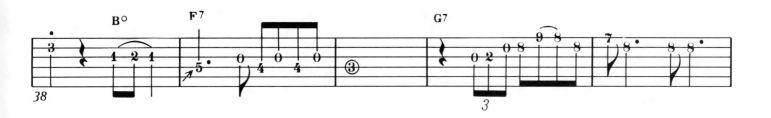

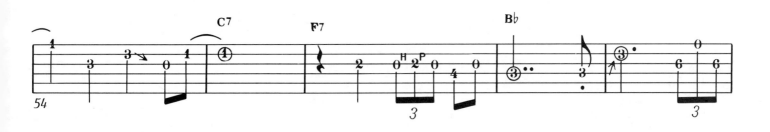

"**Kohala March**" is a typical old Hawaiian march, but with a slick arrangement — lots of fast single-noting interspersed with smooth double stops. This tablature is based on the playing of Pale K. Lua, Sol Hoopii, Jerry Byrd, and myself. (We were not in the same room when we worked it out.) The tempo can range from MM = 112–120, although faster speeds are acceptable when showing off.

The first four measures are an introduction followed by a couple of ragtime-influenced sections leavened with Hawaiian slides and barrages of hiccups. Section III modulates to F for some legato double stops.

In the second version of "**Kohala**," the first section features some dynamic and demanding Sol Hoopii-style triplets, forward rolls, and salvos of syncopated staccato riffs. The third section comes next (sounding like part of the American fiddle tune "**Silver Bells**"), and then the second stanza, this time in the key of B♭. Finish by repeating the introduction and some variety of the first section.

The Kohala Peninsula is in northwest Hawaii and is the birthplace of Kamehameha I.

KOHALA MARCH

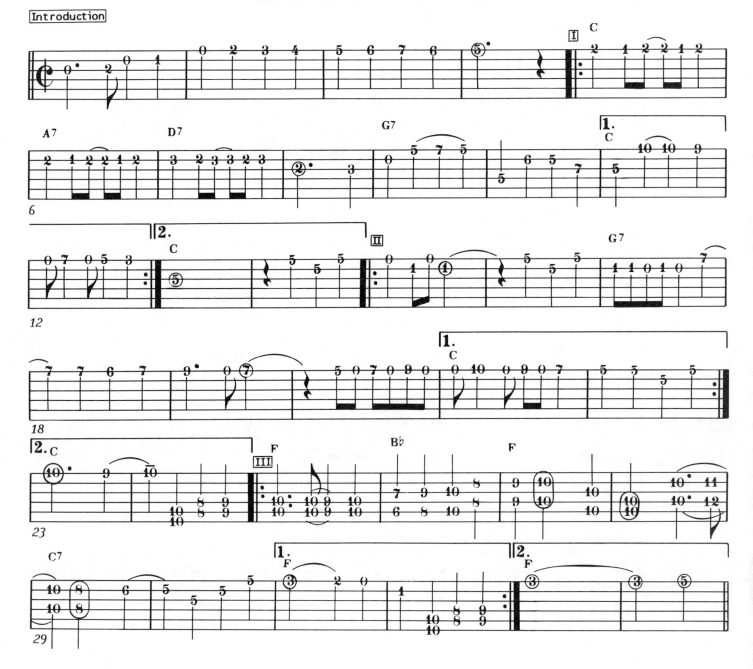

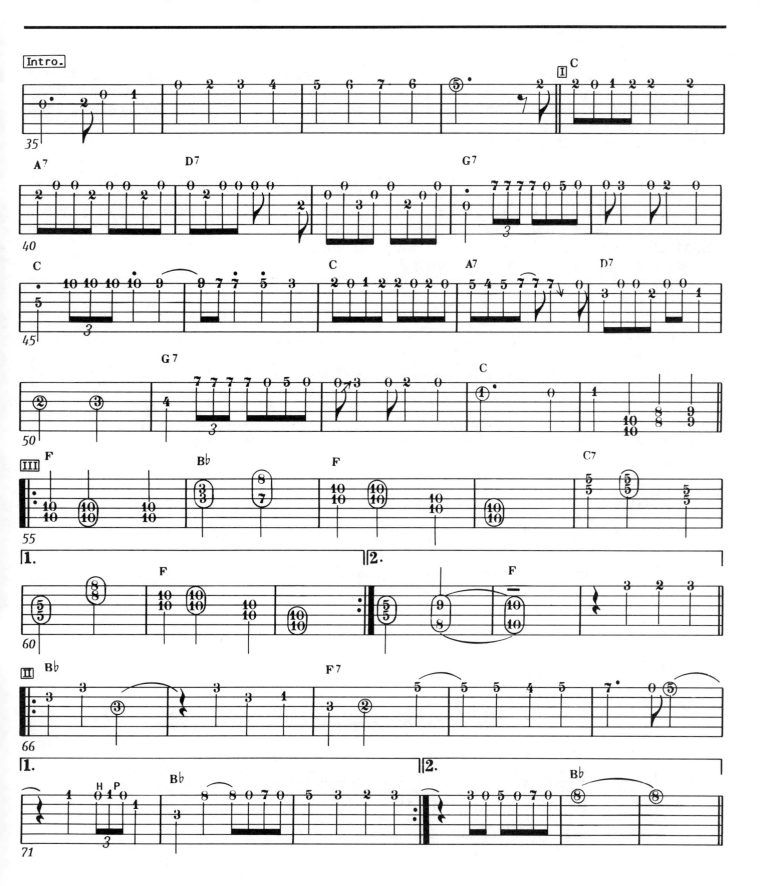

"Hilo March" is one of the great warhorses of the steel guitar. All players have had a go at this at one time or another. The first, slower version is based on a recording by M. K. Moke and should be played at about MM = 104.

It begins with two measures of natural harmonics. Obey the accents to give this passage some life. It is quite syncopated, so take it slowly. The slide to fret 6 in measure 3 is not unlike some melancholic bovine mooing. Slide slo-o-owly from about fret 4 to fret 6. Sliding to string 2, fret 2, gives the same note but not the same pedigree of cow.

Measures 6 and 8 are played legato and lazily, a bit behind the beat. In section II, Moke goes for a very trebly tone by picking the top three strings very near the bridge.

The third section is notable for its use of forward rolls; i.e., a fingering of T-I-M-T-I-M, etc. Moke has invented a particularly inspired application of this simple pattern. Lay the bar flat for the whole section, leaving just the first string open. Play:

as reverse slants and the figures in measure 19 as forward slants. Here is a slight but effective

rhythm variation of measures 19 and 20:

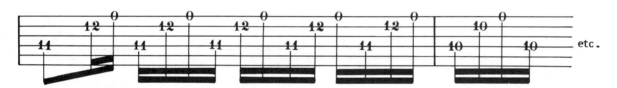

Let the notes overlap on all these rolls. Watch for the string changes in measures 25–28. Moke probably barred these measures the fol-

lowing way. (Thanks to Chris Davis for pointing this out.)

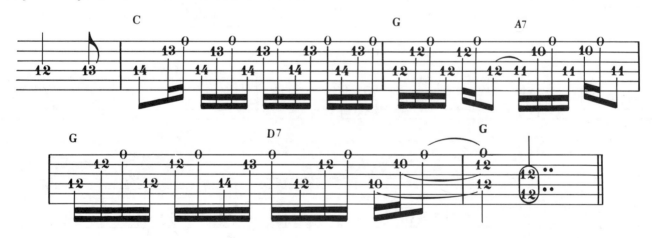

Measure 29 commences a repeat of the three sections of this tune, but now in the key of G with section III in C. The natural harmonics over the C chord in measure 37 sound obscure, but with an accompanying instrument they just pass muster. In measures 43, 45, 51, and 53, use a slant to allow overlap.

"Hilo March #2," based on the now-standard versions by Dick McIntire (1939) and Jerry Byrd, should be played at about MM = 144. It opens with some old-time staccato picking. This passage is filled with a tricky mix of open and closed strings. Section III begins at measure 17 with a masterful exhibition of the creative use of passing-tone double stops. Note the melodic delays in measures 20, 22, 26, and 28. Everything is tabbed on strings 1 and 2 to allow for maximum legato phrasing. Try at least some of this section with artificial harmonics.

The whole schmear ends with an extra third section played in the key of C. It's a five-star, blue-plate special of Hawaiiana!

"**Hilo March**" was composed by Joseph Ae'a for a state visit by Queen Lili'uokalani to Hilo in 1881. The occasion was a potentially disastrous eruption of the Mauna Loa volcano that threatened Hilo. The day after the queen's visit, the lava flow ended. There are about 140 inches of rain each year in the city.

"Hilo 'aina ua lokuloku."

"Hilo of the pouring rain."

Among the many recordings of **"Hilo March"** are *Hawaiian Steel Guitar* (Folklyric 9009), *Steel Guitar Hawaiian Style* (Lehua 7023), and *Hula Blues* (Rounder 1012).

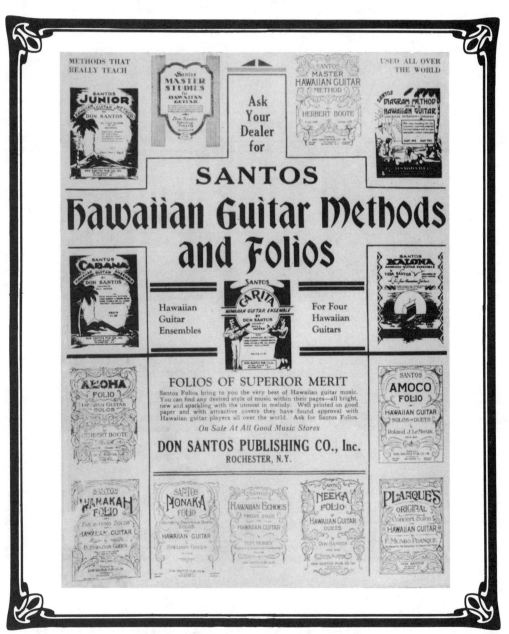

A 1933 advertisement (courtesy of Phil Zimmerman)

HILO MARCH #1

110

HILO MARCH ♯2

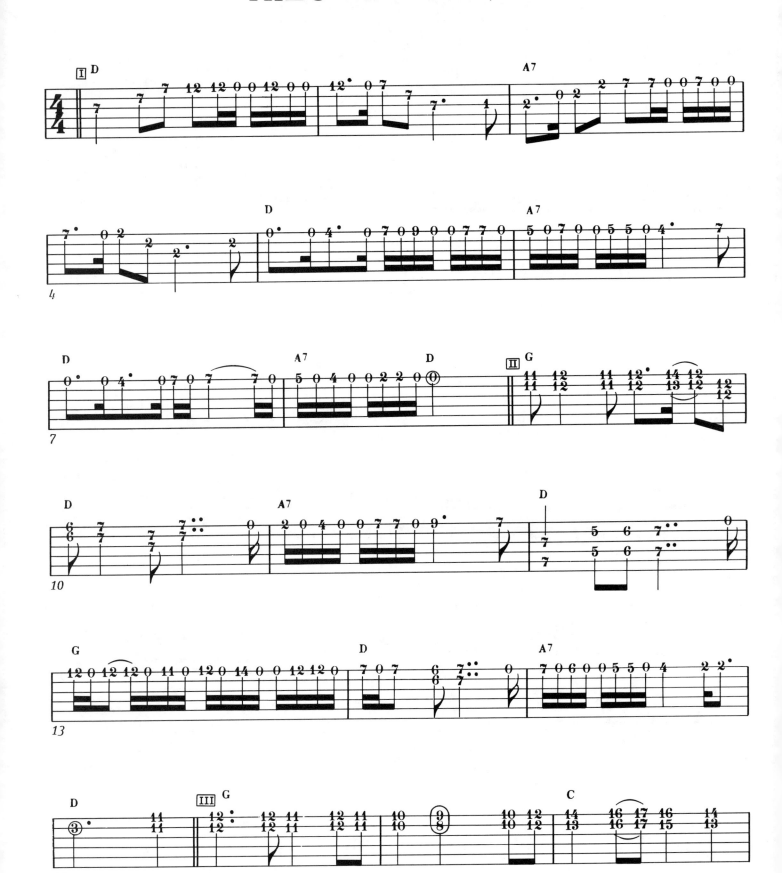

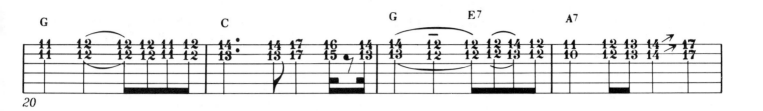

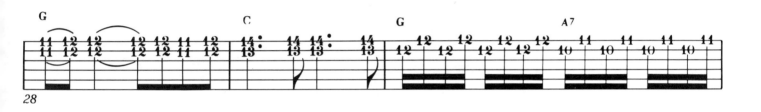

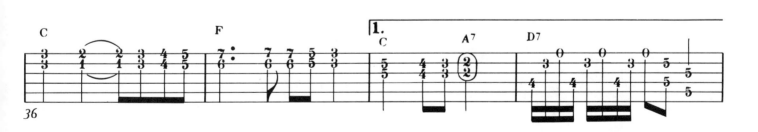
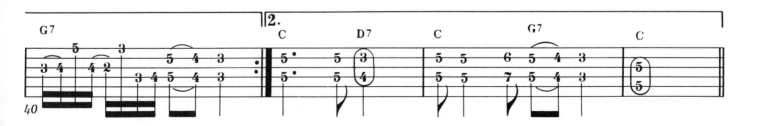

The technique and whole approach for the next piece is quite different from anything else in this book. *"Opihi Moemoe"* is a popular slack-key guitar tune that I adapted for steel. The fifth and sixth strings have been tuned down (giving low bass G tuning).

These bass notes should be picked with the thumb and are indicated in the tablature by downward stems. These low strings keep a steady rhythm, always sounding on strong (foot-on-floor) beats. The middle and index fingers supply the melody and are indicated by upward stems. These melody notes are often placed on upbeats to sound in between the bass notes, giving a strong syncopation. It is probably best to work out the two lines separately and then integrate them. The beats of the two strands of the tablature are aligned to let you see how they interpenetrate. There are a few spots where the thumb supplies the melody, and there the stems are upward; e.g., measures 7 and 9.

Be alert for the two-measure repeats beginning at measures 11, 13, 31, 37, and 39.

Most of this arrangement must be played with the bar tilted to allow the open bass strings to sound. Only a few measures in section II demand that the bar lie flat; e.g., measures 11, 12, 13, and 18.

My version of *"Opihi Moemoe"* (which translates approximately as "lurking limpet") can be found on *Hey Mister Get the Ball* (Shanachie 95004). A slack-key version by Leonard Kwan can be heard on his albums *The Old Way* (Tradewinds 1128) and *Slack Key* (Tradewinds 103). Play at about MM = 136.

Always wipe dry the strings and playing edge of the steel when through playing. Keep guitar in case when not in use. The strings should be raised at the nut $\frac{3}{16}$ of an inch by raising nut, or using an adjuster. See that the strings lay perfectly level. Two positions illustrated by the author in figures 1 and 2 are used for holding the guitar. Position shown by Fig. 2 should be used for ladies and is recommended for gentlemen also. Use a low chair for practice.

Rest forearm lightly on guitar as shown in Fig. 1. Hold right wrist well arched with 4th finger resting lightly on the guitar near the sound hole. Thimbles made of German or sterling silver should be worn open sides up, on the first two fingers. A pick made of same metal or celluloid is worn on the thumb. Let ends of Thimbles and pick entend ⅛ of an inch beyond fingers and thumb.

Fig. 1

Fig. 2

The steel shown in Fig. 3 used and recommended by the author, has following dimensions. Length 3⅜ in. Width ⅞ in. Thickness ¼ in. Weight 4 oz. Sides rough to prevent slipping. Upper ends rounded. Steel should be well tempered and playing edge highly polished. By rubbing on a carpet this edge may be kept in good condition.

O, indicates an open string.

• and •• dots respectively indicate notes are picked with first and second fingers.

x, shows notes are to be picked with thumb. Use alternate fingering in single note playing.

DIRECTIONS for HOLDING STEEL and PLAYING SINGLE NOTES

Grasp the steel (as shown in Fig. 3) with thumb of left hand about one inch to rear of front end. The end of the first finger rests on the further side of the front curved end. Rear of steel rests in the palm of the hand at rear of second finger and is held in position by the first joints of the third and fourth fingers coming firmly under the playing edge. The strings are never pressed down to the frets as the steel acts as the fret.

Fig. 3

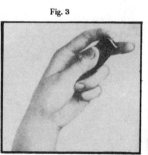

Fig. 4

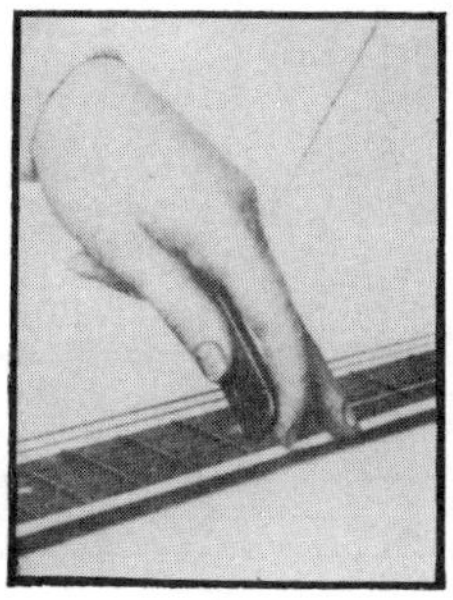

The position of holding the steel in single note execution is shown in Fig. 4. Angle of steel should be so as not to touch the 2nd string. The pressure of the steel varies from a moderate one for single notes to a heavier one in intervals and full chords. All muscles of both fingers and wrist should be well relaxed.

GUARDING THE STRINGS. To guard the strings is to place one or more fingers on them at the rear of the steel. This prevents the disagreeable sound of the strings vibrating against the steel. The guard in single note playing (see Fig. 4) is made with the second finger which rests on the outside edge of the fingerboard keeping its natural curve. A light inward pressure on the string guards it. In playing single notes on the inside strings, guard is made lightly on top of the strings and only the tip of the steel is used.

Some advice on Hawaiian-guitar technique from an early folio, *The Hawaiian Steel Guitar* by C. S. DeLano, published by C. S. DeLano, Los Angeles, California, 1919 (courtesy of Phil Zimmerman)

OPIHI MOEMOE

EXTRA

Music News

EXTRA

VOLUME XXV. No. XIV.

ANY DAY — ANY YEAR

STEEL GUITAR SAVES THE DAY

THERE IS NOT A BRIGHTER STAR IN ALL MOVIELAND

In Hollywood where the stars of the movie and entertainment world shine so brightly, it is difficult for a new star to stand out among the others—it is easy to be just another point of glimmering light.

Long after the story of movies in which Steel Guitars are used, are forgotten, the tunes linger in your mind—like "Sweet Leilani" and "Blue Hawaii"—that is the fascination of the Steel Guitar.

In movieland, the Steel Guitar is always prominent and players always in demand—it would be hard to find at least one set in any of the movie lots in which a Steel Guitar was not being used. The reason this instrument has become such a bright star is that it fits in with such a large variety of scenes and expresses so many emotions.

LORRY LEE

Electric Steel Guitar "Paints" New Tone Colors

Most instruments are limited by the ability and technique of the player, but the Electric Steel Guitar carries on where others leave off. The tone and volume controls give the player a rainbow-like range of tone colors which he can blend and shade to give new life and beauty to his playing, just as an artist uses pastel shades for one effect and striking brilliant colors for another.

With this modern system of teaching, and the fine electric steel guitars now made at any price, even a beginner can add tone color to his playing.

ENTIRE ORCHESTRAS BUILT AROUND STEEL GUITAR PLAYER

What a thrill it is to Steel Guitar students to realize that the instrument of their choice has achieved the seldom acquired position of being the theme for entire orchestras.

Again, it is the distinctiveness of this instrument and the wide range of its musical possibilities that has won for it outstanding fame. The Steel Guitar player is not fitted into the orchestra—the orchestra, the instruments, the arrangements, the type of music and vocalists are selected to fit the Steel Guitar player.

Such orchestras have gained world fame through the versatility and beauty of the Steel Guitar—what other one instrument has done so much to put bands on top!

ALVINO REY

AND NOW COMES TELEVISION

Jack Miller and Andy Sannella were the first artists to use a Steel Guitar on a large chain program — at that time there were few of these instruments on the air, but with the development of better instruments, including Electric Steel Guitars, the number increased so that now one of the most popular instruments for all types of work is the Steel Guitar.

For theme songs, vocal accompaniment, solo effects, and numerous other musical positions, the Steel Guitar fills the bill more completely than any one other instrument could.

And now, Television! Because of the grace with which the player's fingers move from string to string and fret to fret, the Steel Guitar will be an even bigger hit with television.

"Listen To Your Teacher" Guitar Artist Advises Students—

You are fortunate to have such fine teachers, study material and instruments—no wonder the Steel Guitar is the most popular instrument of all. The way is open for you to secure a musical education so that you can play any and all tunes you want—without tedious hours of practicing dry exercises.

Follow your teacher's instructions — take advantage of his years of study and experience — and you are on the right road to musical education and happiness.

ORCHESTRA LEADERS AGREE STEEL GUITAR IS A NECESSITY

Plays Important Part In Orchestra Success

Another orchestra reaches the top ranks, drawing tremendous audiences in the finest theatres, ball rooms, night clubs and hotels!

Just what makes some orchestras outshine all others? The answer is, they get out of the rut—they have that "something" that is different, novel and appealing to the public. Leaders are continually on the look-out for new musical effects, and the Steel Guitar has been the stepping stone of many orchestras to international fame.

The Steel Guitar does many things in an orchestra that no other instruments can duplicate—its distinctive tone adds new beauty to any combination of instruments, its close harmony makes finer arrangements possible, its sparkling effects make any audience stop, look and listen.

Yes, the Steel Guitar has found a very definite place in orchestras and the demand for good players is growing—the student of today is the artist of tomorrow!

Printed in U. S. A.

Courtesy of Phil Zimmerman

"**Pa'au'au Waltz**" is another classic piece by Charles E. King. It is based on an arrangement by Jerry Byrd, but with a layer of my own sensibility added. For example, I have assayed a 3-fret slant at the end of measure 14 to allow a contrary motion on the first and third strings as the discord resolves in measure 15. I am mildly proud of measures 25–26. Because of the particularly tricky combination of tremolo, reverse, and forward slants, the tremolo portion is written out. Continue this effect into the next measure, if you wish. This is another contrary-motion-type maneuver, this time with the lower note going down in pitch and the higher one going up. Devilishly clever, eh?

The chords in section II are almost the same as in the first section. The ⌒ means to stop the indicated rhythm and hold the indicated note(s) for as long as the soloist (that's you) wishes. It is used as a melodramatic, tension-inducing bit of business.

In measure 54 we once again leave most fretboards behind and look for other guitar markings for guidance. If you do not like the fudge slant or string pull, just leave out the note on either the third or fourth strings. In measure 60, to avoid the pull, play the figure as:

Slow down during the last three measures.

"Hoo lale ae ana e ike i ka nani,
o Pa'au'au."

"My heart shall ever yearn for thee,
oh Pa'au'au."

Recordings of this tune can be found on Jerry Byrd's *Steel Guitar Hawaiian Style* (Lehua 7023) and Tony Ku's *Original Hawaiian Classics* (Folkways 8714). Play this beautiful melody at about MM = 80.

PA' AU' AU WALTZ

by C. E. King
and I. U. Iosepa

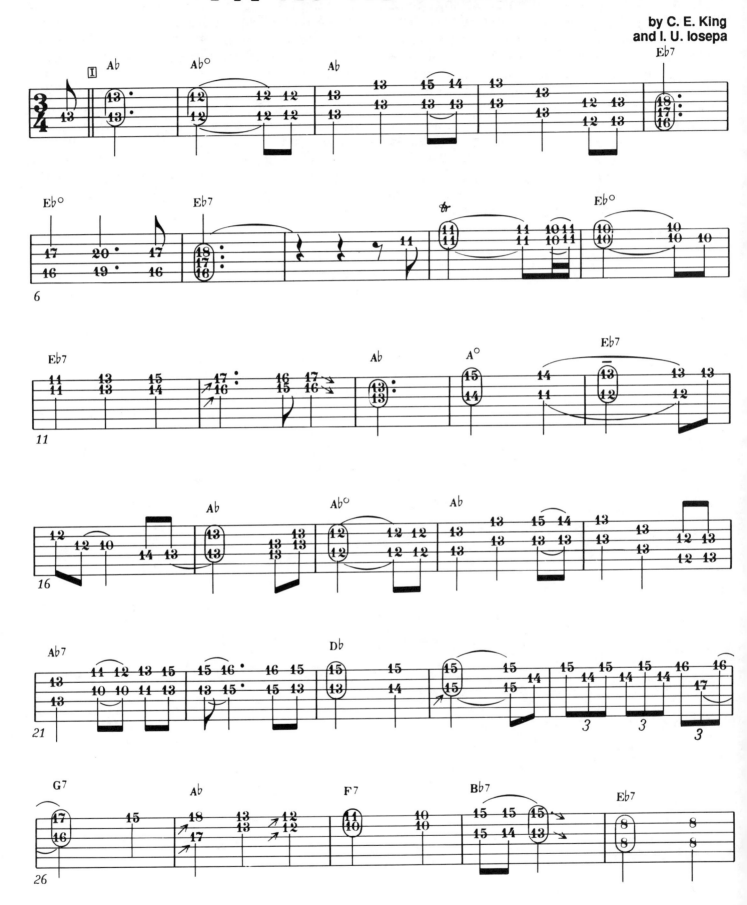

© C. E. King Music Co., New York

120

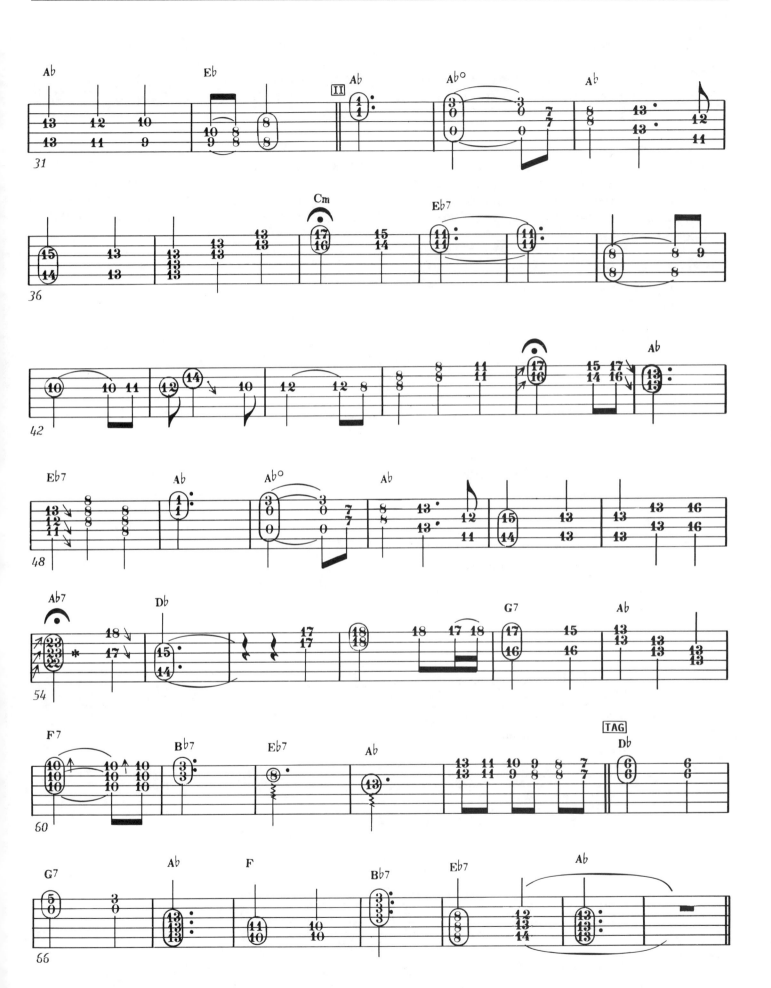

Waltz rhythm entered the Hawaiian ear by way of Western music. **"Kilima Waltz"** is a piece in three sections, reflecting a classical European format. Play it at the lower limit of medium pace, about MM = 96.

Measure 17 presents a dilemma. The tune should be played legato, but the bar has a couple of giant leaps to accomplish. You must take your time, lingering on each note. Even though a tune may be slow, the bar must move very quickly *between* the notes.

The slide at the end of measure 20 is another example of the traditional anticipated slide first described in *"Mai Kai No Kauai."*

Play section II with artificial harmonics the first time, then with standard picking on the repeat. The second time you might add a harmony string 3, fret 9, note to string 1, fret 10, in measure 28.

After a short tremolo to begin section III, measures 39–40 encore some difficult forward to reverse slants of the type exhibited in **"Sweet Lei Lehua."** A less demanding fretting of the same lick (although lacking the opportunity for a smooth legato) would be:

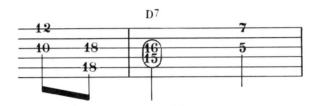

Actually, the hardest thing about these shenanigans is to convince yourself that it can be done. Then start doing it.

The tune ends with a ♭VI chord (G♭) turnaround and a tempo ritard in the last two measures. Recordings of **"Kilima Waltz"** can be found on Jerry Byrd's *Steel Guitar Hawaiian Style* (Lehua 7023) and *Hula Blues* (Rounder 1012). This arrangement is based on the 1948 recording by Bernie Kaai, playing with Danny Kuaana and His Islanders.

KILIMA WALTZ

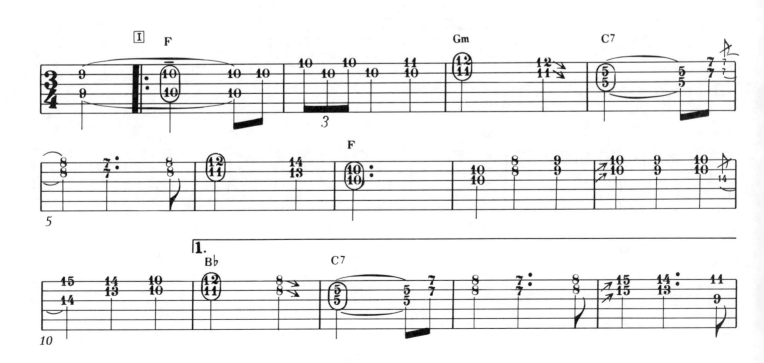

The title *"Tomi Tomi"* refers to a "gentle mauling," the meaning of which is obvious when the accompanying hula is danced. There is nothing gentle or laid back about the pyrotechnics of Sol Hoopii's inspiring arrangement, but his technique is so exemplary that he seems to breeze through it without breaking a sweat. He uses old-time hiccup licks, but with the rhythmic brilliance of the jazz players of his day.

The vocal melody is stated first. Then a series of splendid ripples of notes, unexpected melodic twists, and zany explosions of triplets create seven interesting and demanding variations.

Hoopii does this in the key of C (in A tuning), which transposes to B♭ (in G tuning). He races along at about a 2/4-meter tempo of MM = 116. Watch for all the staccato signs, and hang on for the ride. The unique notation in measures 74–76 gives the approximate frets of a hysterical series of rising triplets, a Hoopii trademark.

Recordings of *"Tomi Tomi"* can be heard on *Sol Hoopii — Volume Two* (Rounder 1025), *Steel Guitar Classics* (Old Timey 113), and *Vintage Hawaiian Music — The Great Singers* (Rounder 1053). The latter contains two other tunes with the same melody, **"Sassy"** and *"Ama Ama."* *"Tomi Tomi"* was written by David Napi, a member of the Henry Berger version of the Royal Hawaiian Band.

The Sol Hoopii Trio (courtesy of Bob Armstrong)

TOMI TOMI ♯ 1

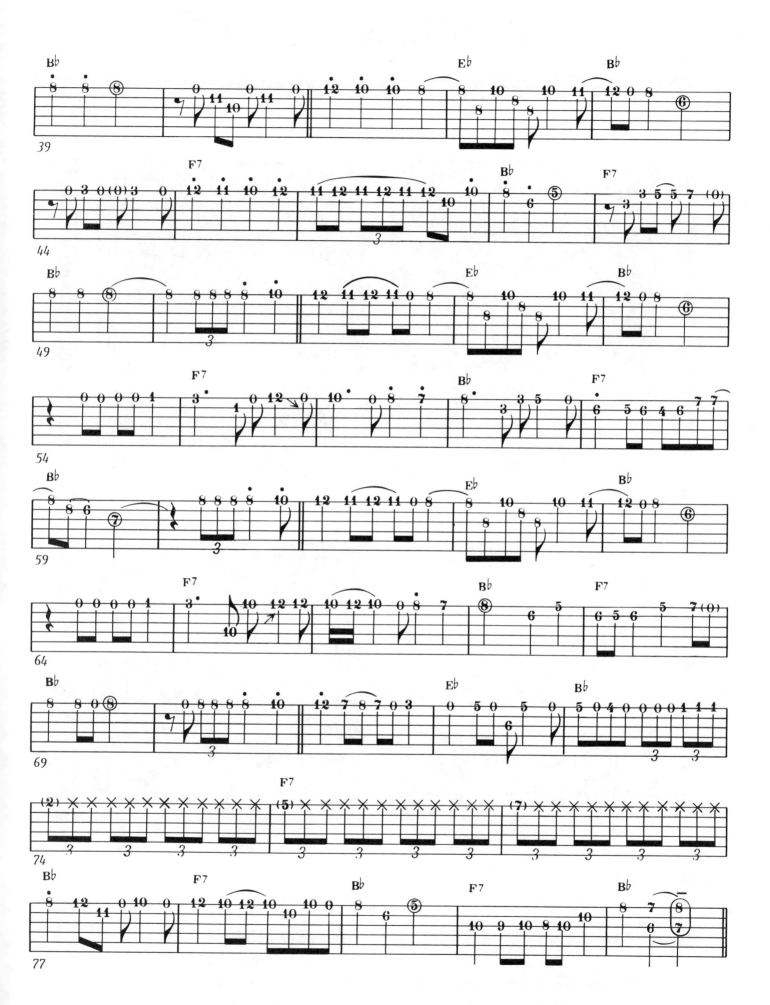

Ways of Holding the Bar

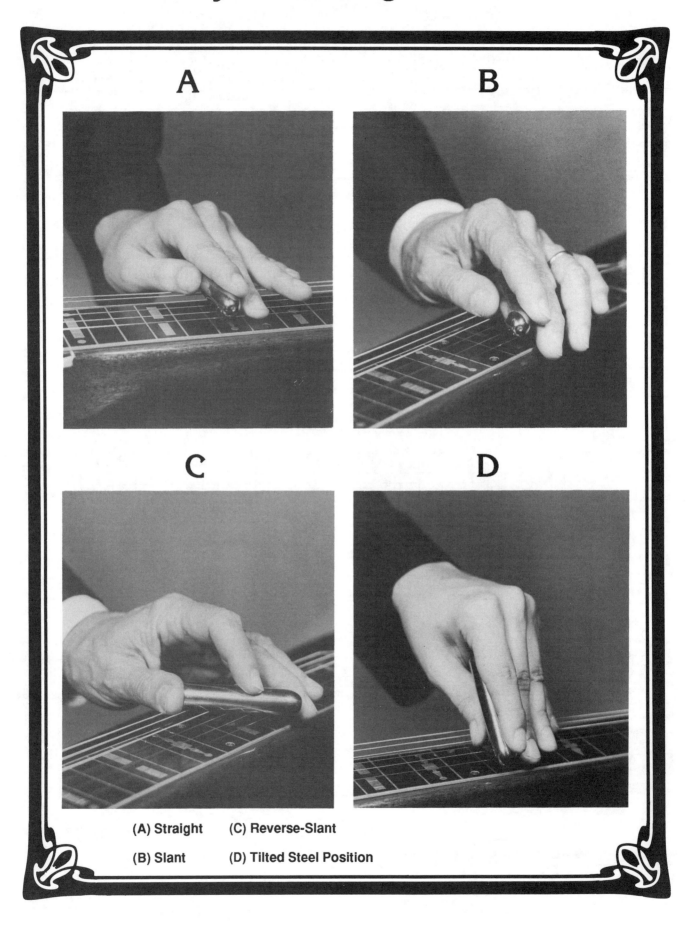

(A) Straight   (C) Reverse-Slant

(B) Slant   (D) Tilted Steel Position

From an old steel guitar method book.

Solomon K. Bright, one-time rhythm guitarist for Sol Hoopii, obviously absorbed a lot of music from the experience and became an excellent steel player in his own right. His version of *"Tomi Tomi #2"* has its own surprises.

The second verse, beginning at measure 11, uses a syncopated gapped-chord approach. The first parentheses in measure 11 indicate a ghosted chord, while the second parentheses and those in measure 13 are the approximate ending fret of the indicated slides. The folderol in measures 30–31 represents three long slides that go from fret 3 to 10 in the space of one beat. Bright does a triplet roll during the beats, approximately reaching the parenthesized frets as shown. To get the flavor, keep a steady bar speed for the 7 frets.

Obey the slur notations to get the right rhythm in the last verse. Play this tune at about MM = 124.

Sol K. Bright (courtesy of Phil Zimmerman)

TOMI TOMI ♯2

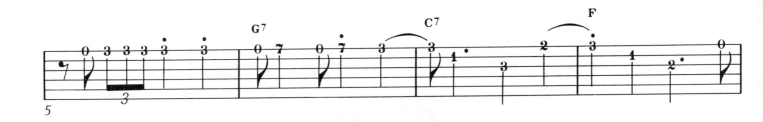

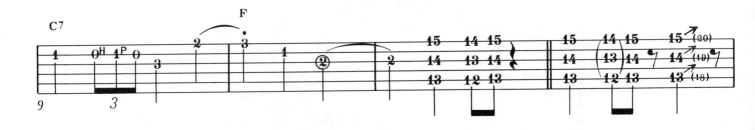

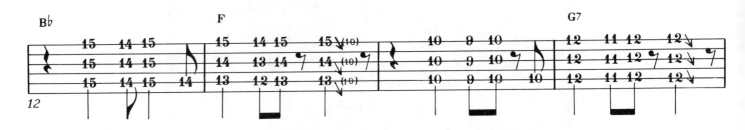

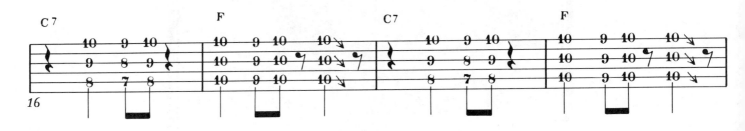

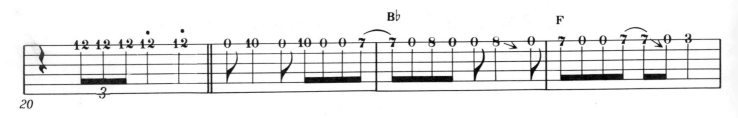

"Honolulu Bound" represents a pinnacle of an offshoot of acoustic Hawaiian guitar music — arranged for the American vaudeville audience of the 1920s. For example, the recording begins with finger picks scraping the sound-hole covers of a National guitar in imitation of a train picking up speed, and the plucking of a string behind the nut, echoing a train's bell. This arrangement is based on the playing of the demurely self-proclaimed King Benny Nawahi. As a teenager he busked with Sol Hoopii in Hawaii before following him to the States. His playing here shows that he was definitely in the same all-star league as Mr. Hoopii. His biography, as reported on the back of his Yazoo album, is a series of triumphs and tragedies.

I think he tuned his guitar to A major and played "Honolulu Bound" in the key of F (in our G tuning, the key of E♭) — more on his tuning presently. Which strings and frets he chose to bar are a mystery. If you analyze what is tabbed here, you will find that similar riffs have been barred differently depending on whim almost as much as rationality. Listen to him on *King Benny Nawahi* (Yazoo 1074) or *Hawaiian Steel Guitar Classics — Volume Two* (Folklyric 9027), and the problem will be evident.

These questions aside, his playing is impressive — full of surprises and rapid salvos of hot licks. The tune seems to be laid out as one long 45-measure opus, with measures 17 and 25 marking the beginning of a couple of subsections. The last 20 measures or so contain an inspired series of wacky double stops careening erratically from chord to chord.

The second verse (based on Nawahi's third variation) begins with a tricky triplet run. Nawahi then proceeds to bounce all over the neck, culminating in the blatant showmanship in measures 72–73. Here he imitates a washboard for a moment with a series of finger-pick taps (the higher-pitched "x") and knocks with (probably) the heel of his barring hand (lower-pitched "x"). Is it time to resurrect this sort of entertainment?

Nawahi lays some twisty melodic turns on our ears. Check out measures 15–16, 46–48, and 60–61. The single-note passages should be played with the tip of the bar, avoiding note overlap. Play this at about MM = 112.

One of my students is convinced that the original recording was in G tuning played in the key of F, and "Honolulu Bound #2" is Chris Davis' idea of what really happened in a small West Coast recording studio in 1929. Chris thinks that the timbre of the notes on the record suggests that much of the playing was done on the thick lower strings. This is especially noticeable in measures 25–34.

Whichever tab is closer to the truth, both are instructive as to how to approach single-note licks without much aid from open strings and some of the things you should consider when you learn tunes on your own. Just realize that you can work out any tune in any key if you do not accept any nonsense about something being too hard.

"King" Benny Nawahi (courtesy of Bob Armstrong)

HOLOLULU BOUND #1

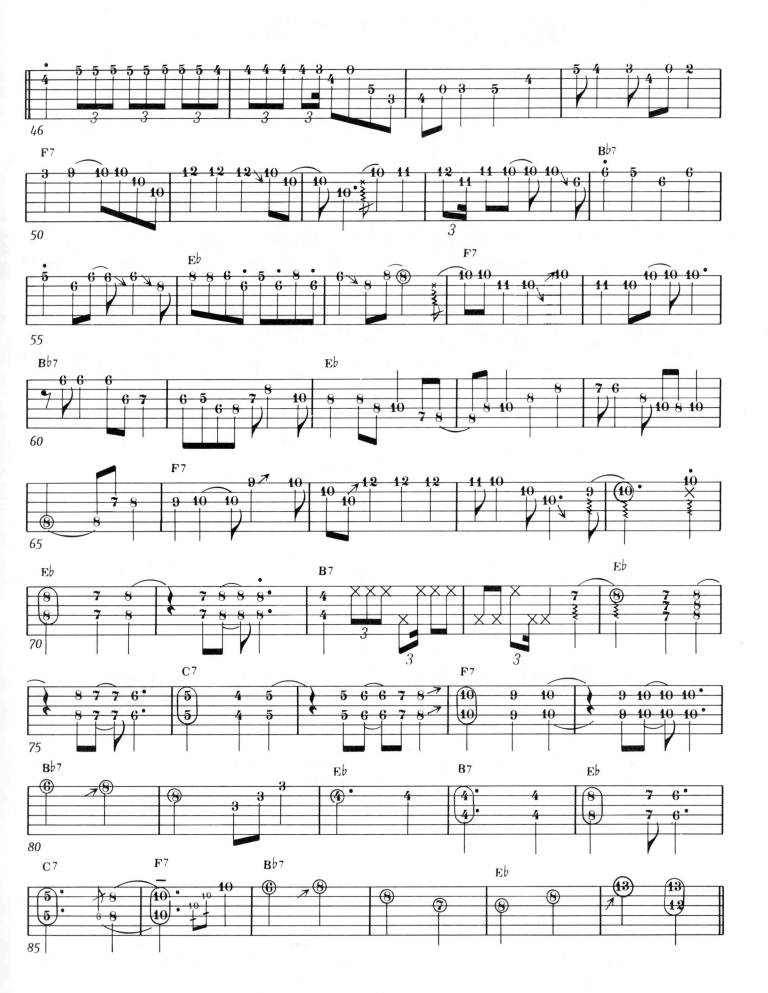

HONOLULU BOUND #2

"Tickling the Strings #1" is a masterpiece of humorous swing licks, courtesy of King Benny Nawahi. The modestly monickered Mr. Nawahi seems to have only partially digested all the nuances of 1920s American pop music, so there are moments when his choice of notes is a bit daft. However, as in "Honolulu Bound," he showcases some formidable technique. There is some astonishing picking here.

In measure 16 the note on the second string is really played between the 9th and 10th frets. It is a matter of interpretation as to what Nawahi meant to bar. Also of aural note are the nice double-stop dissonances of measures 21 and 30. You might prefer to play string 3, fret 6, instead of string 4, fret 11.

The last four measures of section II contain as demanding a riff as will be found in this book.

Almost everything in this arrangement should be played with the tip of the bar.

Nawahi plays this at MM = 100. Versions can be heard on *Hawaiian Guitar Hotshots* (Yazoo 1055) and *King Benny Nawahi* (Yazoo 1074).

For some perverse reason, several years ago I decided to 1) play "Tickling the Strings" in the key of E, 2) change a chord or two, and 3) let the new key lead to whatever melody changes my heart and bar desired. "Tickling the Strings #2" is the result, a first section followed by four versions of section II. They are all similar to but somewhat busier than what Nawahi plays in E♭. I play measures 36 and 44 as slants.

At the very least, this tablature should suggest some key-of-E licks you can appropriate for your own nefarious purposes.

TICKLING THE STRINGS ♯ 1

They don't make music like this anymore (courtesy Robert Gear)

TICKLING THE STRINGS ♯2

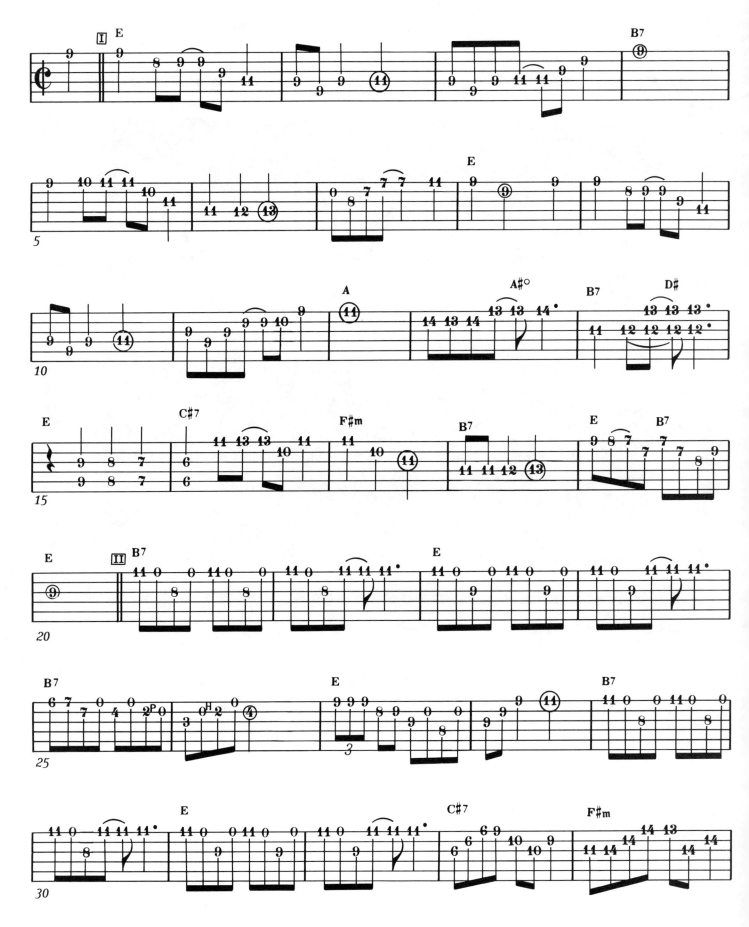

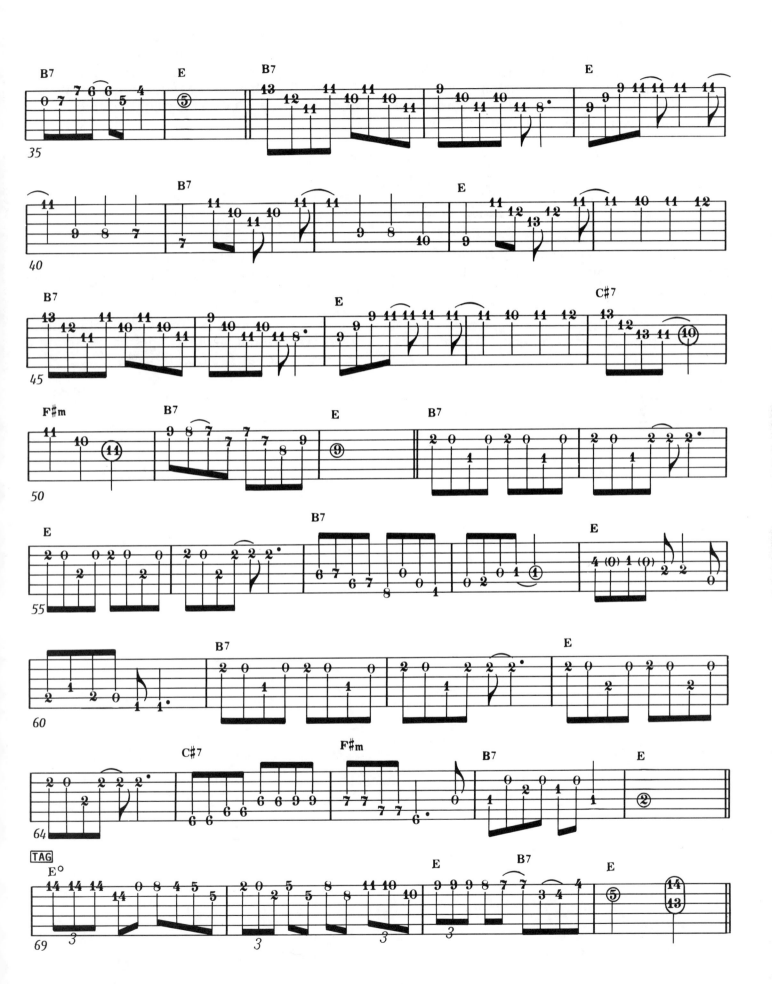

The steel guitarist for Jim and Bob, The Genial Hawaiians, was the only contemporary of Sol Hoopii to challenge his supremacy. Unfortunately, little is known about him. His name may have been Bob Kaai, and he recorded few records, of which only a couple are Hawaiian tunes. In **"Hula Blues #1,"** he exhibits some of his great control of rhythm and steel bar.

The first 16 measures stick reasonably close to the melody. Measure 2 might be fretted as:

In measure 17 he starts showing off. The tablature is only an approximation of his highly syncopated style.

Measure 27 has a Hoopii-like rising triplet run with the usual parenthetical fret markers. Kaai finishes with a blazing, amazingly clean run leading to a third section of the tune. Since he does not do an instrumental version of this part, I have inserted a Sol Hoopii construction from *Sol Hoopii — Volume One*.

Bob's final variation of section I has some blues in measures 41 and 45 and a difficult series of quick double stops in measures 43–44.

A transcription of The Genial Hawaiians' version of **"Home on the Range"** can be found in my instructional *The Dobro Book*.

Jim and Bob, The Genial Hawaiians (courtesy of Phil Zimmerman)

HULA BLUES ♯ 1

by Johnny Noble
and Sonny Cunha

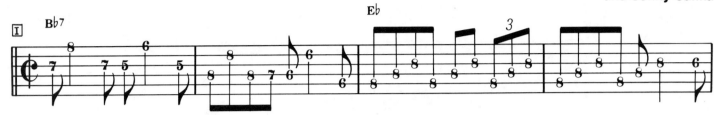

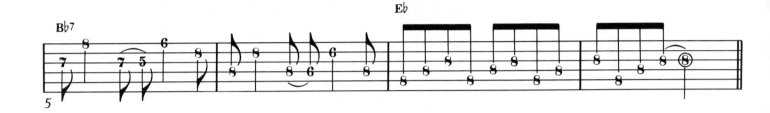

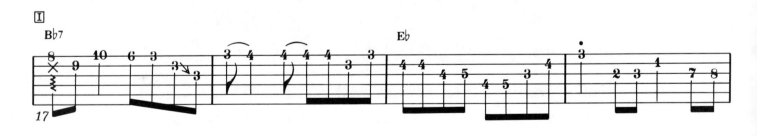

Used by permission.

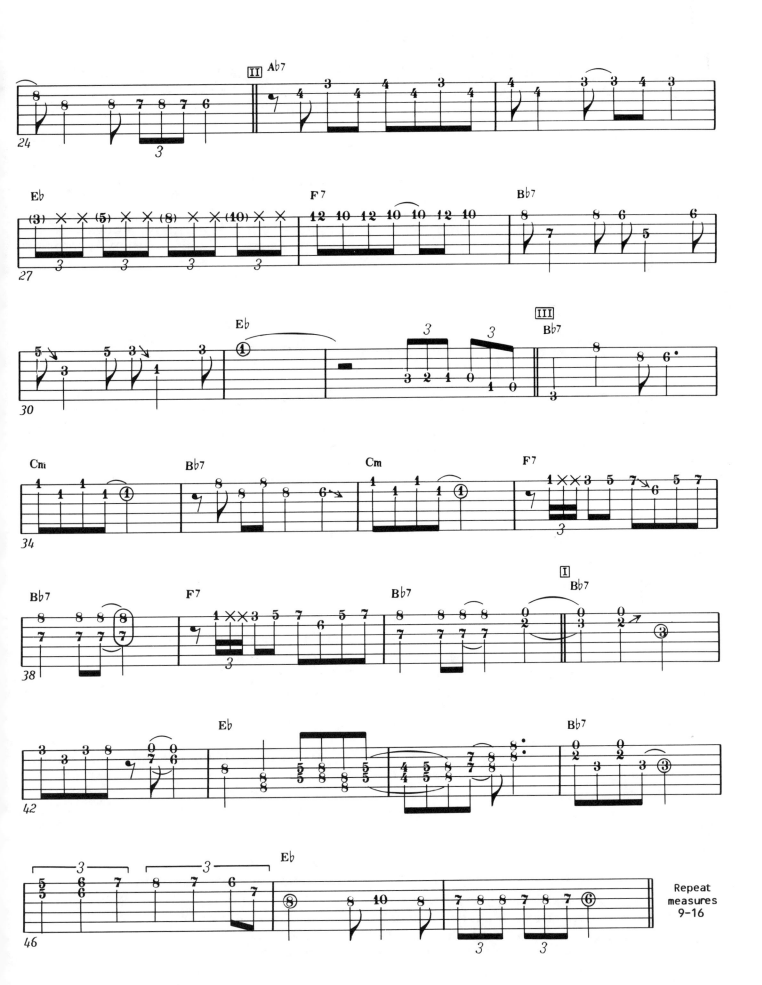

"Hula Blues" is a milestone in the development of the genus of *hapa haole* Hawaiian music. The silly lyrics are in English; and, although not in the least bit a blues, it offers opportunities for blue notes and a pop-music approach. It also has the typical Hawaiian large-interval jumps in section I.

Sol Hoopii's first recording of this tune ("**Hula Blues #2**") has a neat barring of measures 3–4 and a series of very fast triplets in measure 11. This version is somewhat archaic compared to Jim and Bob's, especially in strains like measures 25–32.

Starting in measure 42, though, the temperature is turned up a notch. Hoopii passes through a dissonant B note in measure 51. Just play it with conviction. In measure 53 the second string 1, fret 16, note is actually picked midway between frets 16 and 15. After the string 2, fret 4, in measure 55, the rest is a somewhat inscrutable tag.

Hoopii recorded **"Hula Blues"** twice using variations of his C♯m (our Bm) tuning. One advantage of this is illustrated in the third and fourth measures of the first of those recordings:

This is easier to play and smoother sounding than the equivalent in **"Hula Blues #2."** His third version ("**Hula Blues #3**"), in a sort of Bm7, was played at around MM = 120 in a very relaxed, cool approach to hot soloing. The sections are numbered to conform with The Genial Hawaiians' version.

In measure 5 make an even, continuous slide from fret 1 to 3 to fill in the "x"s. Measure 9 ushers in a very legato first section. You probably do not have to damp the string in this whole part. In section II, Hoopii starts playing the major third (string 1, fret 5) which both Kaai and he flatted previously. Measure 20 adds a C7 chord to the tune. The second triple stop in measure 25 would probably be easiest to play as a fudge slant (as opposed to a string pull), since the bar move can then be a continuous rotation from straight position to 1-fret slant to 2-fret slant (string 1, fret 10, over string 3, fret 8).

The delayed octave slide in measures 27–28 is a signature of modern Hawaiian steel. Start it on the last eighth note of measure 27, make a fast 11-fret glissando, postponing the final resolution to the octave by one beat.

In measure 35, Hoopii commits one of his loony forward rolls. His picking speed comes to about five notes per beat, evenly spaced through the measure. Measures 39–41 illustrate two nice features of this version of Bm7 with a low G note — a full E♭ major chord with the E♭ note on the first string in measure 39, and a full B♭ chord with the B♭ on the sixth string in measure 41, within 2 frets of each other. In between there is a nice walk-up with some anticipated bass-string notes.

The tremolo beginning in measure 49 begins in basic triplet timing, but Hoopii drags behind by the third beat, alternating strings at a slightly slower rate and arriving at the indicated fret a fraction late. This is a good example of controlled toying with the beat. By measure 51, Hoopii is back on the beam. In measure 55 he drags again, rushes ahead, and relaxes into the backup rhythm in measure 55.

The two slides in measure 64 are attacked like those of measure 42 in **"La Rosita #2"** — not languid, but sharp, fast, and short.

Recordings of **"Hula Blues"** can be found on *Hula Blues* (Rounder 1012), *Vintage Hawaiian Music — Steel Guitar Masters* (Rounder 1052), *Sol Hoopii — Volume One* (Rounder 1024), and *Sol Hoopii — Volume Two* (Rounder 1025).

"While you hear the mellow steel guitars
Moaning softly under tropic skies,
You wriggle, you giggle,
you wiggle to the 'Hula Blues.' "

Jim and Bob, The Genial Hawaiians (courtesy of Tony Todaro)

HULA BLUES ♯2

**by Johnny Noble
and Sonny Cunha**

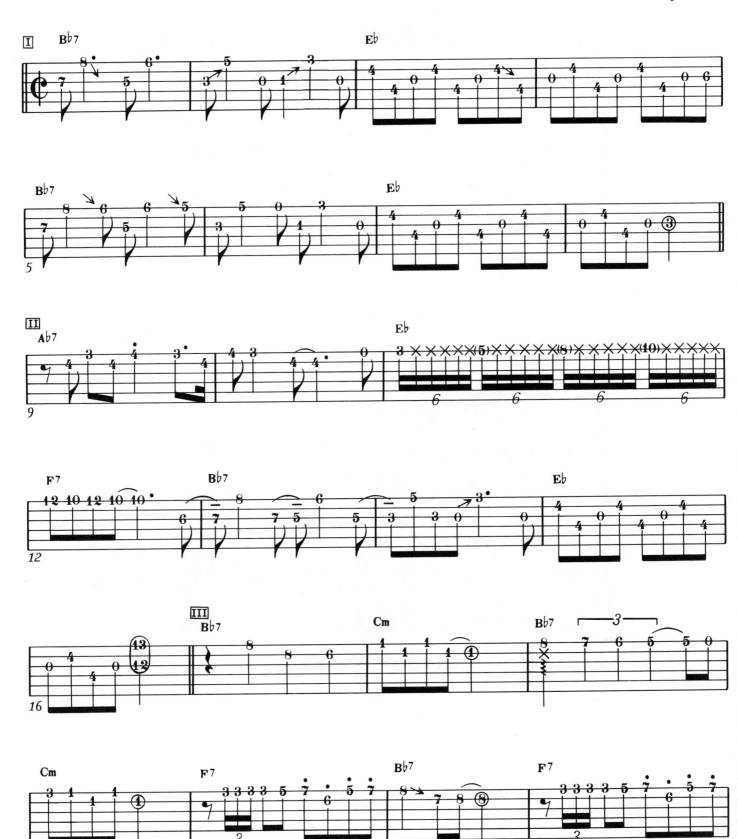

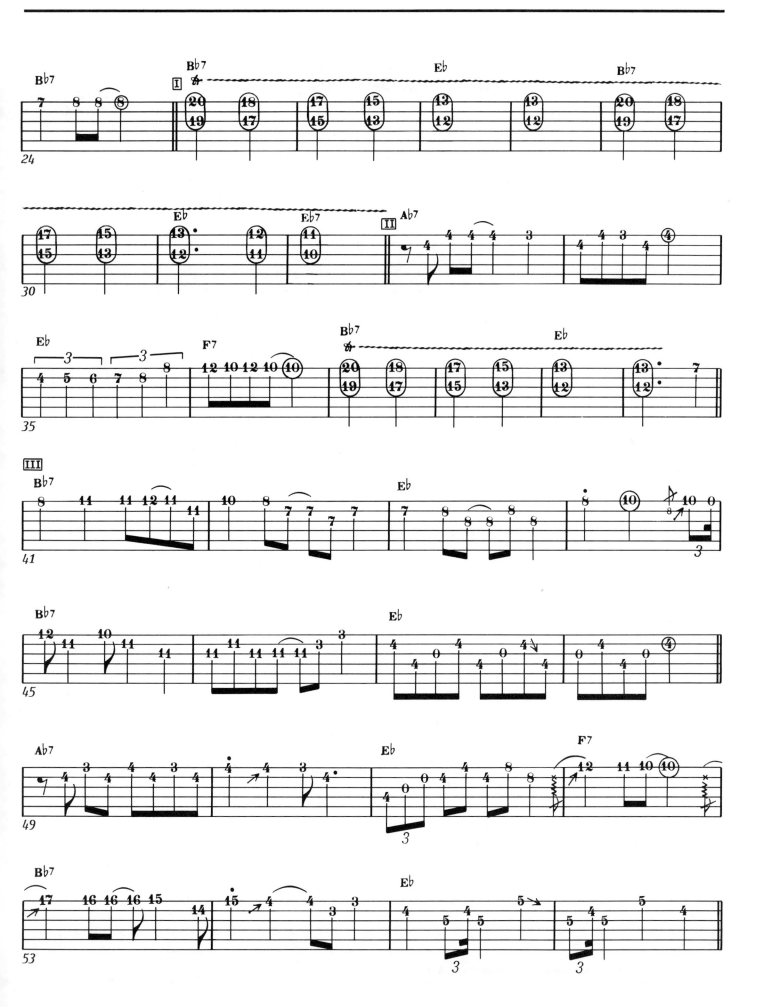

HULA BLUES #3

by Johnny Noble
and Sonny Cunha

An Incomplete Guide to the Pronunciation of the Hawaiian Language

Twelve letters from the Latin alphabet were adapted to cover all the sounds of the Hawaiian language. "H," "k," "l," "m," "n," and "p" are pronounced close to the English.

"W" is pronounced like the English, except as a "v" after "i" and "e," and when beginning the last syllable of a word.

"A" is pronounced as in "above" or "far."

"E" is pronounced as in "bet" or "weigh."

"I" is pronounced like the "ee" in "see."

"O" is pronounced as in "no."

"U" is pronounced like the "oo" in "moon."

' indicates a glottal stop as in "oh-oh."

All vowels are pronounced. Stress is usually placed on the next-to-last syllable of a word. When the second syllable of a two-syllable word is a diphthong, it is accented, as in "leHUA."

Bibliography

1. *Hawaii — The Sugar Coated Fortress* by Francine DuPlessix Gray (Random House, 1972)
2. *Shoal of Time* by Gavin Daws (MacMillan Corp., 1968)
3. *Hidden Hawaii* by Ray Riegart (Ulysses Press, 1979)
4. *Ancient Hawaiian Music* by Helen Roberts (Dover Publications, 1967)
5. *Na Mele O Hawaii Nei* collected by Samuel Elbert and Noelani Mahoe (University of Hawaii Press, 1970)
6. *Nineteenth Century Hawaiian Chant* by Elizabeth Tatar (Pacific Anthropological Records #33, Bishop Museum, Honolulu, Hawaii)
7. *Hawaiian Music and Musicians* edited by George Kanahele (University Press of Hawaii, 1979)
8. *Da Kine Sound: Conversations with People Who Create Hawaiian Music* by Robert Kasher and Burl Burlingame (Press Pacifica, 1983)
9. *Strains of Change: The Impact of Tourism on Hawaiian Music* by Elizabeth Tatar (Bishop Museum Press)
10. *Hawaiian Music in Its History* by Ruth Hausman (Charles E. Tuttle Co., 1968)
11. *Olelo No'eau* by Mary K. Pukui (Bishop Museum Press, 1983)
12. *The Hawaiian Monarchy* by Maxine Mrantz (Aloha Graphics and Sales, 1974)
13. *The Dobro Book* by Stacy Phillips (Music Sales Corp., 1977)
14. *The Dobro Chord Book* by Stacy Phillips (Music Sales Corp., 1988) *The latter two books are available from me at 36 Cromwell Hill Road, Monroe, NY 10950.*
15. *Steel Guitar Classics* by Robert Gear (Pineapple Productions, 1982)
16. *Folk Songs Hawaii Sings* by John Kelly (Charles E. Tuttle Co., 1963)
17. *Popular Musics of the Non-Western World* by Peter Manuel (Oxford University Press, 1989)
18. *Teaching the Musics of Six Different Cultures in the Modern Secondary School* by Luvenia George (Parker Publications)
19. *Musics of Many Cultures* edited by Elizabeth May (University of California Press)
20. "Ha'ilono Mele" *(Hawaiian Music Foundation Newsletter)*
21. "Musical Ornamentation as History: The Hawaiian Steel Guitar" by Mantle Hood (article in *Yearbook for Traditional Music Volume 15*)
22. "Hawaiian Music" by Robert Gear (article in *Frets* Magazine, May 1981)
23. "Towards a Description of Precontact Music in Hawaii" by Elizabeth Tatar (article in *Ethnomusicology,* September '81)
24. The liner notes of the reissue albums mentioned in the discography are very informative.

Discography

Your local pop-record shop probably does not stock an extensive array of Hawaiian music, so here is some guidance. The first two establishments on this list specialize in all aspects of the steel guitar and are deserving of your support.

a) Scotty's Music, 9535 Midland, St. Louis, Missouri 63114
b) Tom Bradshaw's Steel Guitar Products, P.O. Box 931, Concord, California 94522
c) Down Home Music, 10341 San Pablo Ave., El Cerrito, California 94530
d) Roundup Records, One Camp Street, Cambridge, Massachusetts 02140
e) The House of Records, Ala Moana Shopping Center, Honolulu, Hawaii

1. **Sol Hoopii**
   a) *Master of the Steel Guitar — Volume One* (Rounder 1024)
   b) *Master of the Steel Guitar — Volume Two* (Rounder 1025)
2. *King Benny Nawahi* (Yazoo 1074)
3. **Kalama's Quartette** *Early Hawaiian Classics* (Folklyric 9022)
4. **Tony Ku** *Original Hawaiian Classics* (Folkways 8714)
5. **Reissue collections**
   a) *Hawaiian Steel Guitar* (Folklyric 9009)
   b) *Hawaiian Steel Guitar Classics — Volume Two* (Folklyric 9027)
   c) *Hawaiian Guitar Hotshots* (Yazoo 1055)
   d) *Hula Blues* (Rounder 1012)
   e) *Vintage Hawaiian Music — Steel Guitar Masters* (Rounder 1052)
   f) *Vintage Hawaiian Music — The Great Singers* (Rounder 1053)
6. **Bob Brozman** (there are a few Hawaiian-style cuts on each album)
   a) *Blue Hula Stomp* (Kicking Mule 173)
   b) *Snapping the Strings* (Kicking Mule 322)
   c) *Hello Central . . . Give Me Dr. Jazz* (Rounder 3086)
   d) *Devil's Slide* (Rounder 3112)
7. *The Tau Moe Family with Bob Brozman* (Rounder 6028)
8. *The Emersons* (Mountain Apple 1008)
9. *Roy Smeck* (Yazoo 1062)

10. **Jerry Byrd**
    a) *Byrd in Hawaii* (Maple 1002)
    b) *Steel Guitar Hawaiian Style* (Lehua 7023)
    c) *Byrd of Paradise*
    d) *Hawaiian Beach Party*

The last two and other Byrd albums are available from Tom Bradshaw (see above for address).

11. **David Kelii** *Hawaii's Own* (Lehua 46A)
12. **Hal Aloma** *A Musical Portrait of Hawaii* (Columbia 538)
13. **Jules Ah See** *Hawaii Calls — Favorite Instrumentals of the Islands* (Capitol 4N-1670)
14. **Vintage Original Hawaiian Classics** (Vintage 1003)
15. **Stacy Phillips** *Hey Mister Get the Ball* (Shanachie 95004)

Matses Steel Guitars (20 Essex Street, West Boxford, MA 01885) is one of the few current makers of lap steels

Some Steel-Guitar Clubs & Conventions
(compiled by DeWitt Scott)

This list is by no means exhaustive, and not every club's main focus is Hawaiian music; but it can be a means of making contact with like-minded people. There are still some fine Hawaiian-style players out there, scattered about. These clubs help bring them together. Some publish occasional newsletters.

1. **Steel Guitar International**
   (DeWitt Scott, 9534 Midland, St. Louis, Missouri 63114) *This convention is the big one. Mostly country oriented, but plenty of Hawaiian music, too. Scotty is the world's leading maven of steel guitars.*

2. **Hawaiian "Echoes of the Islands"**
   (Jimmy Hawton, 122 Rubicon Street, Napa, California 94558)

3. **Aloha International Steel Guitar Club**
   (P.O. Box 24284, Minneapolis, Minnesota 55424) *This club has a newsletter and a yearly convention.*

4. **Hawaiian Steel Guitar Association**
   (Box 3156, Bellingham, Washington 98227) *This club has a newsletter and a biennial convention.*

5. **Hawaiian Steel Guitar Association**
   (Frank Miller, 228 Madison St., Joliet, Illinois 60435)

6. *Hawaiian Music Newsletter*
   (Fred Gagner, 10432 East Flintlock, Tucson, Arizona 85749)

7. **Jerry Byrd's** *Ho'olaue'a*
   (P.O. Box 15026, Honolulu, Hawaii 96830) *This is a yearly gathering.*

8. **Pedal Steel Guitar Association**
   (P.O. Box 248, Floral Park, New York 11011)

9. **British Steel Guitar Festival**
   (Gerry Hogan, "Treetops," Harts Lane, Burghclere, Newbury, Berkshire, England)

10. **Steel Guitar Australia**
    (Peter Williams, 10 Simia Street, Toowoomba, Queensland 4350, Australia)

11. **Steel Guitar of Canada**
    (Al Brisco, 9201 Yonge Street, Richmond Hill, Ontario L4C 6Z2, Canada)

12. **Japan Steel Guitar Convention**
    (Mistuo Fujii, 8-80-13 Sunagawa Cho, Tachikawa City T190, Japan)

Ha'ina Ia Mai Ana Ka Puana
"Thus Ends the Story"

The chapter title is the phrase that introduces the final verse of traditional-type *meles* (alternately translated as "tell the summary refrain," "tell the theme," or "the tale is told"). So here are a few last exhortations and advice:

1. Record the accompanying chords onto a tape, and practice along to it. It is best to make the tape with a metronome to keep solid time.

2. Isolate, analyze, and memorize any licks that you like. Transpose them to other keys, and apply them to several different musical situations.

3. Here are some other tunings that have been favored by some steel players. The strings are listed from high to low, with lower-pitched versions in parentheses so you can see the similarity to tunings used in this book:

a) F#9: E-C#-G#-E-A#-F#
(E9: D-B-F#-D-G#-E)

b) B11: E-C#-A-F#-D#-B
(G11: C-A-F-D-B-G)

c) E13: E-C#-G#-E-D-B
(D13: D-B-F#-D-C-A) or
E13: E-C#-B-G#-E-D
(D13: D-B-A-F#-D-C)

d) A6: E-C#-A-F#-E-C#
(G6: D-B-G-E-D-B)

Tunings c and d probably would necessitate some restringing of the lower strings, even in the lower-pitched versions. The top four strings are very similar in these tunings, and the lower strings are generally used infrequently, and then only as part of strums. For most one- and two-string playing, a plain old major-chord tuning is sufficient.

There is a Hawaiian guitar course published by Jerry Byrd that has some tablature in these tunings. Contact Scotty's Music or Tom Bradshaw's Steel Products (see discography for addresses) to find whether it is still available. It comes with a Japanese translation.

4. Buy some of the records listed in the discography, and listen critically and carefully to the steel playing. There is no substitute for listening and playing in massive doses. Unfortunately, many great players have been under-represented or left out of the book due to lack of space and suitable available recordings. These include Sam Koki, Andy Iona, Jules Ah See, David Kelii, Bob Kaai, and others who may be undeservedly obscure.

I believe you have enough musical information to keep you busy for quite a while. Take the difficult sections slowly, and have patience.

Aloha.

Stacy Phillips
March 18, 1991

NOTES

NOTES

NOTES

NOTES

Great Music at Your Fingertips